THE GREAT DOCTORS

by ROBERT SILVERBERG

WE cannot say who the first doctor was because he is "an unknown hero of civilization." Perhaps he lived in Europe or in Africa; he may have been a medicine man or a priest; he may have been his own first patient. What we do know is that Hippocrates was *not* the earliest doctor. There were several Egyptian doctors long before him. This would place Hippocrates at the halfway point between Imhotep, who is believed to have lived in 3000 B.C., and Dr. Jonas Salk.

Robert Silverberg has prepared a careful personality characterization of some of the most important doctors who have made history in the past and some of the doctors who are exceptional in the medical profession at the present time. Included are the life stories and medical accomplishments of Lister, Harvey, Fleming, Jenner, Cushing, Salk, Sabin, and others. Direct quotations from the doctors are included as well as quotes about them from prominent people of their times.

Some diseases which were thought insurmountable centuries ago are today solved by trips to the doctor's office for some type of immunization or therapy. The story of medicine has no end, and there will always be new doctors to take their place with Hippocrates and the other great doctors as long as there is disease and death for medical research to combat. Perhaps the young readers of today will be among those credited with providing knowledge toward the cure of cancer and heart disease, only two of our greatest life takers.

The Great Doctors

We cannot say who the first
pocrates was *not* the earliest doct
long before him. This would pla
tween Imhotep, who is believed
Jonas Salk.

Robert Silverberg has prepare
of the most important doctors w
some of the doctors who are exc
present time. His narrative is mad
the doctors as well as quotes abc
times.

The story of medicine has no e
to take their place with Hippocr
as there is disease and death for

The Great Doctors

By Robert Silverberg

G. P. Putnam's Sons • New York

For Stephen—M.D. '65

SECOND PRINTING

© 1964 by Robert Silverberg
All Rights Reserved
Published simultaneously in the Dominion of
Canada by Longmans Canada Limited, Toronto
Library of Congress Catalog Card Number: 64–13041
MANUFACTURED IN THE UNITED STATES OF AMERICA
12216

Contents

I swear by Apollo Physician, by Asclepius, by Health, by Panacea and by all the gods and goddesses, making them my witnesses, that I will carry out, according to my ability and judgment, this oath and this indenture. To hold my teacher in this art equal to my own parents; to make him partner in my livelihood; when he is in need of money to share mine with him; to consider his family as my own brothers, and to teach them this art, if they want to learn it, without fee or indenture. . . . I will use treatment to help the sick according to my ability and judgment, but never with a view to injury and wrong-doing. . . . I will keep pure and holy both my life and my art. . . . Into whatsoever houses I enter, I will enter to help the sick, and I will abstain from all intentional wrong-doing and harm. . . .

——From the Hippocratic Oath

Introduction: The Story of Medicine

THERE HAVE always been healers among us. Medicine is as old as pain itself, as old as humanity.

We can never know the name of the first healer. He is lost to us in the mists of the past. Like the inventor of the wheel, like the man who first tamed fire, he must remain an unknown hero of civilization.

In the ancient Mesopotamian city of Nippur, four thousand years ago, a scribe wrote in cuneiform on a tablet of clay the prayer of a king's daughter: "Pain has seized my body. May God tear this pain out!"

Four thousand years ago! But only yesterday, really. Mankind's past goes back at least a hundred times as far. The doctor who healed that princess in Nippur is far closer to our own time than he was to the time of humanity's first doctor.

Maybe that doctor lived in the forests of Europe, a few hundred thousand years ago, or perhaps in the steaming jungles of Java even earlier, or in the sprawling tablelands of South Africa. He was probably a priest as well as a doctor. His people must have considered him a man of supernatural power. His first patient may have been himself. A slashed finger may have become infected and puffy. It throbbed with pain.

"If I cut the finger off," this unsung genius must have thought,

9

"the demon that possesses it will not be able to invade the rest of my body!"

And so this priest with the infected finger took a sharpened flint blade in his good hand. He spread his demon-possessed hand out on a flat rock. He struck.

The edge of the flint cut through layers of skin and layers of infection and struck the bone. And still the unflinching man hacked away until the offending finger lay at his feet. Blood spurted from the wound. But perhaps he plunged his hand into boiling water, or covered the wound with cool mud.

And he recovered. Word spread that a man had cast a demon from his body with a stone knife. Surgery was born!

Surgery was the first branch of medicine that man practiced successfully. Other prehistoric medical practices were mostly magical: the wearing of amulets, the beating of sacred drums. But surgery was real. There was nothing mystical about it. And, amazingly, it often served to cure.

One of the most common surgical operations in the prehistoric world was, incredibly enough, brain surgery. We know this because we have found human skulls thousands of years old in which a portion of the skull was removed and then began to heal—proof that prehistoric patients often survived the operation.

Removal of portions of the skull is called *trepanning*. We know that it was practiced in many parts of the ancient world—particularly in ancient France, but also elsewhere in Europe, Asia, and Africa, and in the New World in the kingdoms of the Aztecs, Mayas, and Incas. Since there was no contact between these farflung regions in ancient times, we have to assume that the idea of trepanning occurred to many men in a great many places independently.

The operation was performed pretty much the same way everywhere. The patient, who might be suffering from severe headaches, fever, or some other ailment that indicated the presence of a "demon" in the skull, would be held down by the strongest men of the tribe.

Maybe the patient would be given an anesthetic, in the form of beer or some herb drug.

The surgeon of the tribe would approach, carrying his razor-keen flints. His assistants would stretch the patient's scalp taut. With a bold, confident swipe, the surgeon would slash away hair and skin, until an oval patch of the skull itself showed.

Then, bending to his task, the surgeon would make a series of scratches with the flint, cutting a shallow groove in the bone. Soon it was possible to lift away an entire segment of the outer shell of bone, an inch in diameter. Underneath lay a softer layer of bone, more easily removed. The surgeon had to work carefully as he scratched the last slivers of bone from the site. He knew from past experience that if he cut into the gray membrane underneath the last layer of bone, the patient would die.

Skilfully he finished his task. The patient lay unconscious from the pain, but still alive. A patch of brain was exposed through the hole in the skull. The demon had an avenue for escape, now.

The operation was over.

Now the surgeon would put the skin of the scalp back into place, and perhaps would bind bark and leaves over the wound. If the patient lived, as many of them did, the bone would slowly heal. Soon the patient would be healthy again.

The people of the past used trepanation not only for medical but for magical reasons. When a skull had been fractured, and splinters of bone threatened life, trepanation was used. But in one burial ground in France, 40 out of 120 skulls had been trepanned. There could not have been that many brain injuries in one tribe, so trepanation must have had a mystical significance. Or perhaps it was just a tribal fad!

We know little or nothing about prehistoric medicine but for the evidence of skeletons bearing signs of amputation or trepanation. Doubtless there were magic potions and formulas in use, but we will never know. In France, in a cave known as the Cave of the Three Brothers, there is a drawing on a wall, showing a weird being who must have been the tribal sorcerer and doctor. He wears the skin of an animal, with antlers on his head and painted stripes on his arms and legs. Certainly this must have been the healer of the tribe, this fantastic and grotesque figure. His is the first known portrait of a doctor—25,000 years ago.

About 4000 B.C., a revolution swept the world, the revolution known as civilization. In Egypt, in Mesopotamia, and in China, men began to gather together in cities. They learned how to raise their own food, how to tame animals to serve their needs. They developed complicated languages, and found means of writing down their thoughts, passing them on to succeeding generations. In these three civilizations, medicine flourished and became an art.

Pictures on the walls of Egyptian tombs show us surgical operations as they were practiced nearly five thousand years ago. Papyrus records from Egypt tell us how advanced medicine was along the Nile in the days of the Pharaohs. We even have several medical textbooks from Egypt. The oldest and best of these is called the Smith Papyrus, because it was discovered by an archaeologist named Edwin Smith in 1862. It dates from about 1600 B.C., but it seems to be a copy of an earlier text that may go back another thousand years or more.

The Smith Papyrus is a remarkable scientific document. It is largely a surgical text, and it was written by a surgeon who was a master of his trade. There is no magical mumbojumbo in this millennia-old text. The author had no use for charms, amulets, or incantations. He believed in careful observation, in close examination. There are forty-eight cases described. The author knew that the brain was the seat of intelligence. He recognized the importance of the heart, though he did not understand the circulation of the blood. He wisely recommended letting a disease take its course, rather than rashly attempting risky remedies. He understood the pulse, and probably counted it. This is a sample of the kind of anatomical knowledge the unknown author of the Smith Papyrus had:

If thou examinest a man having a gaping wound in his head, penetrating to the bone, smashing his skull, and rending open the brain of his skull, thou shouldst palpate the wound. Shouldst thou find that smash which is in his skull like those corrugations which form in molten copper, and something therein throbbing and fluttering under thy fingers, like the weak place of an infant's crown before it becomes whole—when it has happened there is no throbbing and fluttering under thy fingers until the brain of his [the patient's] skull is rent open—and he discharges blood from both his nostrils, and he suffers with stiffness in his neck. . . .

But not all Egyptian medicine is this accurate. We have a second medical text, called the Ebers Papyrus, discovered by George M. Ebers in 1872. The Ebers Papyrus was probably written about 1560 B.C., fifty years after the Smith Papyrus, but it may have originally been compiled many hundreds of years after the Smith.

The Ebers Papyrus offers more than 877 remedies for diseases. These remedies are of three types: medicines, magical spells, and surgical operations. The "medicines" recommended are mostly worthless. They consisted of things like worms' blood mixed in fresh milk.

The surgical advice was more reliable. It showed that the Egyptians relied on cauterization—red-hot iron applied to the source of disease —as well as the surgical knife. Here is the instruction for diagnosing a tumor of the flesh:

When thou comest upon a tumor of the flesh in any part of the body of a person and thou dost find it like skin on his flesh; it is moist; it moves under thy fingers save when thy fingers are held still, then its movement is caused by thy fingers. So shalt thou say: "It is a tumor of the flesh. I will treat the disease since I will try to cure it with fire, as the metal-worker cures."

Sometimes the knife is recommended for cutting away tumors, with the cautery used afterward to check the bleeding. Fatty tumors were to be dealt "with the Knife, taking care of the Blood-Vessels the while."

But the Ebers Papyrus is ridden with incantations and warnings against demons. Compared with the earlier Smith Papyrus, it is a foolish and unscientific document. Looking at the two texts, it is possible to see the sharp decline in Egyptian science and medicine over the centuries. In Egypt science reached its summit about 2500 B.C. and then gradually deteriorated. A craft founded on observation and understanding gave way to one built on superstition and fear.

In the Tigris-Euphrates Valley, meanwhile, a different group of people was creating a fascinating civilization. These were the Sumerians, who were even more advanced than the Egyptians in the ways of science. About 2500 B.C., invaders entered the land of Sumer and conquered the Sumerians, who were absorbed into the new nations that arose, first Babylonia, and then, to the north, Assyria. But the conquerors were careful to learn the civilized ways of the defeated Sumerians.

Most of what we know of Sumerian medicine was actually written down thousands of years after the Sumerians passed from the scene. Ashurbanipal, King of Assyria, compiled a magnificent library about 650 B.C., which has been discovered and translated by archaeologists. This library contains many copies of Sumerian texts that were almost 2,000 years old in Ashurbanipal's time—nearly as distant from his day as he is from ours! These texts show us that Sumerian medicine, like Egyptian, was a mixture of the practical and the magical.

One Babylonian text tells us a great deal about the way the medical profession was regulated in Mesopotamia. This is the Code of Hammurabi, the laws of the great king of Babylonia who ruled about 1700 B.C. These are the sections of Hammurabi's Code dealing with medicine:

> If a physician operates on a nobleman for a severe wound with a bronze lancet and saves the man's life, or if he opens up the eyesocket of a nobleman with a bronze lancet [to remove an abscess] and saves the nobleman's eye, he shall receive ten shekels of silver.

If it was a commoner, he shall receive five shekels.

If it was a slave, the owner of the slave shall give two shekels of silver to the physician.

If a physician operates on a nobleman with a bronze lancet and causes the nobleman's death, or if he opens up the eyesocket of a nobleman and destroys the nobleman's eye, they shall cut off his hand.

If a physician operates on a slave with a bronze lancet and causes his death, he shall make good slave for slave.

If he opens up a slave's eyesocket with a bronze lancet and causes his death, he shall pay one half his value in silver.

These harsh clauses must certainly have discouraged surgeons from making rash operations. But they also tell us much about the advanced state of surgery in Babylonia 3,700 years ago.

The third great center of ancient civilization was China. Here, medicine seems to have been even more a matter of magic and mumbojumbo than in Egypt and Mesopotamia. The most important medical techniques of old China were *acupuncture* and *moxibustion.* Acupuncture is the sticking of needles into the body at specific points to heal specific ills. Moxibustion is the burning of an aromatic herb over the ailing parts of the body. It is interesting that the Chinese Communist Government, in its hatred of everything Western, has revived these two ancient magical techniques of medicine.

The accounts of early Chinese medicine that we have do not impress us as being very scientific. For instance, here is one dating from 300 B.C.:

One day two men, Lu and Chao, called on [the surgeon Pien Ch'iao]. He gave them a drug and they were unconscious for three days. Pien Ch'iao operated and opened their bodies and explored the heart; after removing and interchanging their organs he gave them a wonderful drug and the two men went home recovered and healthy.

Such miracles of surgery are unlikely. But in ancient India, on the other hand, surgery did rise to great heights. The *Sushruta Samhita,* a medical book written about 600 B.C., gives an interesting record of medical techniques dating back perhaps as far as 1200 B.C.

Eight general types of operation—scraping, puncturing, extracting, suturing, etc.—are described, and more than 100 different surgical instruments are discussed in detail. Indian surgeons were given instructions in anatomy by dissecting dead children. (Adults were cremated after death.) The emphasis on training through actual experience is different from that of Egypt and Mesopotamia in their later days, where doctors were content to rely on the word of others who had come before.

This excerpt from the *Sushruta Samhita* shows the kind of training Hindu doctors were getting 3,000 years ago:

The art of making specific forms of incisions should be taught by making cuts in the body of a gourd, watermelon, or cucumber. The art of making cuts either in the upward or downward direction should be similarly taught. The art of making excisions should be demonstrated practically by making openings in the body of a full waterbag, or in the bladder of a dead animal, or in the side of a leather pouch full of slime or water. . . .

It is startling to see how advanced these Hindu surgeons were, even at the very modern practice of plastic surgery. Hindus wore rings through pierced ears, and sometimes the weight of the ring would split the earlobe into two parts. There were as many as fifteen ways of repairing this damage. Consider this one, if you thought that skin grafts were a development of our century:

Ganda-Karna consists in slicing off a patch of healthy flesh from one of the regions of the cheeks and adhering it to one of the severed lobes of the ears which is more elongated on its anterior side than the other.

The ancient Hindus also practiced nerve surgery, opened the abdomen to relieve intestinal blockages, and sutured the bowel when ruptured by injury. But this phenomenal surgical skill began to decline in the sixth century B.C., when Buddhism gained influence. Buddha forbade sacrificial offerings of animals, and taught that it was wrong to come in contact with blood, pus, and disease.

As a result, doctors lost touch with reality. They could no longer rely on firsthand experiments and observations. All medical research stopped. Such textbooks as had already been written became holy, and it was forbidden to question the teachings of the ancients.

Wherever doctors fail to keep in contact with their work, wherever they begin to rely on written texts instead of the evidence of their own eyes, medicine turns into a ritualistic and unscientific thing that is more related to magic than to knowledge. It happened in Egypt, it happened in India, and we will see it happen later in Europe.

But while medicine was declining in the older civilizations of the world, it was undergoing a rebirth elsewhere. On the islands of Greece, rough-hewn and rocky, washed by the blue Mediterranean, men of medicine were arising to heal the suffering. Among them was one of the greatest doctors the world has ever known—Hippocrates of Cos.

1

Hippocrates: The Father of Medicine

Wно is the earliest doctor whose name we know?

Not Hippocrates. Not by many thousands of years. There was an Egyptian named Imhotep, who is supposed to have lived about 3000 B.C. Not only was Imhotep a doctor, but he was a statesman as well, grand vizier to the Pharaoh Zoser. And he was an architect, too. Legend tells us that Imhotep designed the first of all the pyramids, the step-pyramid at Sakkara.

Imhotep's life is shrouded in legend. After his death, he was worshiped as a god in Egypt. If he really lived at all, he lived as far before Hippocrates as Hippocrates is before us. That makes Hippocrates a halfway point between Imhotep and Dr. Jonas Salk, on the scale of history. It is something to consider with awe.

We know the name of another Egyptian doctor. He is Sekhetenach, chief physician to Pharaoh during the Fifth Dynasty, about 2700 B.C. There is a monument to Sekhetenach at Sakkara. It tells us that he "healed the king's nostrils," and therefore Pharaoh wished him "a long life in happiness."

Thirteen centuries later, in Greece, there flourished Asklepios, whom the Romans called Aesculapius. What he really accomplished, we can never know, for his life has been transformed into a legend. As the Egyptians had done with Imhotep, so did the Greeks with

Asklepios: They made him a god. Legend said he was the son of Apollo, that he was raised on the slopes of Mount Pelion by the centaur Chiron, who taught him the healing arts. In manhood, the sick came from far and wide to be treated by Asklepios, until he over-stepped the boundaries of his art by raising the dead to life. This was presumptuous, and Zeus slew him with a thunderbolt.

Temples of Asklepios sprang up all over Greece. To them came suffering ones, placing themselves in the care of the priests of the cult. These pilgrims were told to sleep, and that Asklepios would come to them in dreams and heal them. It was a kind of faith healing, and evidently it often succeeded, much as miracles of healing are some-times worked at religious shrines today. But the cult of Asklepios had little science to it, however great a doctor Asklepios himself may have been. In time, it became priest-ridden, superstition-mongering.

Homer mentions Asklepios, and Asklepios' two sons, Machaon and Podalirius, doctors themselves. As the centuries passed, other Greeks formed their own theories about disease and healing. There were many schools. The followers of Asklepios believed in faith, in psychological curing. Others, the rhizotomists or root diggers, made drugs from plants, some of them worthless, others of great value. We have many names of these Greek doctors: Ctesias, Euryphon, Chrysippos, Alcmaion.

But these men—though they were unquestionably real, not semi-legendary characters like Imhotep and Asklepios—are little more than names to us. We know where they lived, we have a fragment or two of their writings, but they have no flesh-and-blood reality for us. They do not stand out as *people*.

Hippocrates does. He is the first man in all medicine whose per-sonality we know. From the works that bear his name, and from the things others of his day said of him, we can all but see him in the flesh, short but stately, wise, bearded—The Father of Medicine.

In Plato's day, there were two chief schools of medicine in Greece, one at the promontory of Cnidos, the other on the nearby island of

Cos. The Cnidian doctors were famous for their highly specialized studies. The great Roman doctor Galen said of them that they recognized seven diseases of the bile and twelve of the bladder, so obviously they dwelt too strongly on small details, since at that time no doctor could have distinguished so many diseases so minutely! Yet much was valuable about the work of the doctors of Cnidos.

A greater medical school, though, was to be found on Cos, a lovely, fertile island that produced grapes and silk as well as outstanding doctors. Hippocrates, who was born there about 460 B.C., did not found the school of Cos. He is merely its best-known representative. It was ancient when he was born.

Why is this man called the Father of Medicine, if he lived 2,500 years after Imhotep, and if he did not even found his own school of medicine?

Perhaps the term, Father of Medicine, is too dramatic to be really accurate. But Hippocrates earned it through his long devotion to healing. He summed up all that had gone before him and gave it form and balance. He was not so much a pioneer as he was a codifier, an organizer. He does not stand at the beginning of Greek medicine, but at its climax.

Though he is supposed to have been short of stature, his figure is a towering one that looms above the ages as a guide for all physicians who followed after him. Even today, 2,500 years since his time, doctors everywhere, when they begin their medical careers, take the Oath of Hippocrates, the oath found on the first page of this book. And it is the hope of every doctor to measure up to the great standard set by this beloved Greek.

Hippocrates was the son of a doctor, Heraclides, who was his first teacher. The accounts of Hippocrates' life are unreliable, since they were written six hundred years after he died, but we are told that he studied under several Greek philosophers, including Democritus, and then traveled widely throughout Greece and the surrounding lands.

We are told that he cured the king of Macedon after all court physicians had failed; that he freed the city of Abdera from the plague;

that he went next to Athens, where a plague also raged. At Athens, Hippocrates noticed that the blacksmiths, who toiled all day in front of a roaring fire, seemed immune to the plague. Was there a connection between fire and health?

"Build huge bonfires," he told the people of Athens. "Keep them blazing night and day."

The epidemic subsided. Athens erected a statue of Hippocrates in gratitude, inscribed, "To our rescuer and benefactor, Hippocrates."

His fame spread to other lands. Artaxerxes, King of Kings, King of Persia, the enemy of Greece, begged him to become his court physician, but the patriotic Hippocrates refused. He spent his old age teaching medicine on Cos, seated under a great plane tree surrounded by young followers, and died in his eighties, about 375 B.C.

Fables surround his grave. On Cos, they will show you the plane tree under which Hippocrates is supposed to have taught, and they will tell you, "His tomb is there. After he died, a swarm of honeybees came to nest over his grave, and their honey cured all diseases."

There may be no more truth in all these stories than in the tale of Asklepios and the centaur. The only contemporary of Hippocrates who makes any mention of him is Plato, and Plato tells us very little. In the dialogue *Protagoras,* Plato mentions the well-known physician Hippocrates of Cos, who teaches medicine for a fee. And in *Phaedrus,* one character asks another if it is possible to understand the human soul without the knowledge of nature, and the answer is given that "according to Hippocrates the Asclepiad," there can be no understanding of the soul without an awareness of the body. And in Aristotle's *Politics,* written not long after Hippocrates' death, Aristotle refers to Hippocrates as a great physician. These scanty references are the only mentions of Hippocrates dating from his own time.

All that we can be sure of in the life of Hippocrates is that he lived during the Golden Age of Greece, the time of Plato and Socrates and Pericles, and that he taught medicine wisely and well and was esteemed as the greatest doctor of his day. The rest is uncertain.

It is even uncertain who wrote the many medical texts that bear the name of Hippocrates as author. There are dozens of books in the body of work known as "The Hippocratic Corpus." Some of these texts are known to have been written several hundred years after Hippocrates lived. A few are out-and-out forgeries. At least one is thought to have been written by Hippocrates, son of Gnosidicos, grandfather of the great Hippocrates. Some were written by Hippocrates' own pupils, and they probably represent teachings taken directly from the master's words.

One thing seems fairly sure: Not a single page of the Hippocratic Corpus was actually written by Hippocrates. But much of it is the work of his disciples and clearly derives from his own teachings. The Hippocratic Corpus is full of bold and courageous ideas.

Although he was an Asclepiad, a member of the Cult of Asklepios, Hippocrates had no use for the faith-healing ideas of the Asclepian priests. Sickness, he said, was not sent by the gods and could not be taken away by prayer or the influence of dreams. Sickness had a material basis. There was a physical cause for every disease. If that cause could be found, Hippocrates taught, the disease could be cured.

All this sounds very obvious and commonplace to us today. In Hippocrates' time, though, fanciful theories on disease were prevalent. The simple idea that there was a direct link between disease and a physical cause was revolutionary.

"What is disease?" men asked Hippocrates. "What is health?"

He had his theories. They were based on the ideas of earlier Greeks, and though his ideas seem strange and fantastic to us today, they represented an advance over the thinking of the priests of Asklepios. Hippocrates taught the theory of the four humors:

> The body of man has in itself blood, phlegm, yellow bile, and black bile. . . . Now, he enjoys the most perfect health when these elements are duly proportioned to one another in respect of compounding power and bulk and when they are perfectly mingled. Pain is felt when one of these elements is in defect or

excess, or is isolated in the body without being compounded with all the others.

When one of the four humors grew out of proportion to the others, medical treatment was needed. For example, an excess of blood required bloodletting, and this practice continued on nearly into our own days. One of the famous victims of bloodletting was George Washington. He caught a cold while riding on his Mount Vernon estate in winter, and his doctors were overenthusiastic about drawing blood from his body. They weakened him until he died of loss of blood.

Purging or bloodletting could be used to adjust the balance of the four humors. But Hippocrates realized that such remedies were not always helpful. "Nature is the healer of disease," he declared. "Nature itself finds means and ways. The task of the physician is to help nature in any way he can, not to try to do too much himself, but to make it possible for nature to effect her cure."

But how could the doctor know the workings of nature?

There was only one way, Hippocrates taught: by observation, by examination. The doctor could not rely on books to do his work for him. He had to study the patient. Textbooks could assist, but they could not substitute for firsthand experience.

To guide those who followed after him, Hippocrates or his disciples set down case histories, in which the course of a disease was vividly described, so that other doctors could compare their observations and conclusions with those of Hippocrates. This, from the Hippocratic book *Epidemics,* is a typical case history:

In Thasos the wife of Delearces, who lay sick on the plain, was seized after a grief with an acute fever with shivering. From the beginning she would wrap herself up, and throughout, without speaking a word, she would fumble, pluck, scratch, pick hairs, weep and then laugh, but she did not sleep; though stimulated, the bowels passed nothing. She drank a little when the attendants suggested it. Urine thin and scanty; fever slight to the touch; coldness of the extremities.

Ninth day: much wandering followed by return to reason; silent.

Fourteenth day: respiration rare and large with long intervals becoming afterwards short.

Hippocrates' descriptions of disease have rarely been matched. I like to think he wrote them himself, but, even if they were set down by one of his gifted pupils, it seems to me that the hand of the master himself is on them. One of the most famous is called the *Hippocratic facies*—the description of the appearance of a man whose body has been long racked by disease. It shows a superb observer at work:

In acute diseases the physician must make his observations in the following way. He must first look at the face of the patient and see whether it is like that of people in good health, and particularly whether it is like its usual self, for this is the best of all; whereas the most opposite to it is the worst, such as the following: nose sharp, eyes hollow, temples sunken, ears cold and contracted and their lobes turned out, the skin about the face dry, tense, and parched, the color of the face as a whole being yellow or black, livid or lead-colored. If at the beginning of the disease the face is such and if the other symptoms do not yet permit making a prognosis, one must inquire whether the patient has been sleepless, whether he had strong diarrhea, or whether he has suffered from hunger. If any of these causes be admitted, the condition may be considered less threatening. The crisis will come in the course of a day and a night if the condition of the face was due to any such cause. But if the patient does not tell of any such cause, and if the condition does not clear up within that period, you must know that this is a sign of imminent death. . . .

This description comes from the Hippocratic book *Prognosis*, which many experts feel was actually written by Hippocrates himself. I hope it is so. Such a superb piece of writing should not be permitted to go down the ages in anonymity.

Another of the important Hippocratic works is the one on *Wounds in the Head,* which tells of trepanning and brain surgery. There is also a short book called *In the Surgery,* thought to have been written by Hippocrates' doctor son Thessalos, which contains much that is sound and valuable. Hippocrates taught that wounds should be washed in boiled or filtered water and that dressings should be of new linen. The surgeon's hands and nails were to be kept clean, "the nails neither to exceed nor come short of the fingertips."

Hippocrates carefully specified the kind of light to be used in the operating chamber and declared, "Let those who look after the patient present the part for operation as you want it, and hold fast the rest of the body so as to be all steady, keeping silence and obeying their superior."

One weakness of the Hippocratic writings is the lack of true knowledge of human anatomy. The Greeks revered the human body, and it was considered sacrilegious to dissect it. A doctor who dared to open a body merely to gratify his curiosity was risking the wrath of the gods.

And so Hippocrates and those of his time could only guess at the structure of the body. They could dissect animals, of course, and try to extend their conclusions to human beings. They could gain some insight by operating on wounded soldiers, or by studying animals at sacrificial altars. But, by and large, Hippocrates had only a sketchy idea of the interior of the body, the functions of the organs, muscles, and nerves.

Yet he knew, at least, that the brain was the seat of consciousness. In his writings we find:

> From the brain only arise our pleasures, joys, laughter, and jests, as well as our sorrow, pains, griefs, and tears. . . . I hold that the brain is the most powerful organ in the human body. . . . Eyes, ears, tongue, hands, and feet act in accordance with the discernment of the brain. . . . To consciousness the brain is the messenger.

In his works we find aphorisms, general observations on medicine and on life. The most famous of these is, "Life is short, the art is long, opportunity fleeting, experience treacherous, judgment difficult. It is not enough for the physician to do what is necessary, but the patient and the attendants must cooperate as well and circumstances must be favorable."

And there is this bit of advice to doctors:

I urge you not to be too unkind, but to consider carefully your patient's superabundance or means. Sometimes give your services for nothing, calling to mind a previous benefaction or present satisfaction. And if there be an opportunity of serving one who is a stranger in financial straits, give full assistance to all such. For where there is love of man, there is also love of the art.

For some patients, though conscious that their condition is perilous, recover their health simply through their contentment with the goodness of the physician. And it is well to superintend the sick to make them well, to care for the healthy to keep them well, but also care for one's self, to observe what is seemly.

There are occasional courageous confessions of failure, as in this, found at the conclusion of the case history of a patient who had died:

I have written this down deliberately, believing it is valuable to learn of unsuccessful experiments and to know the causes of their failures.

The Hippocratic Corpus is a hodgepodge of varying quality. Some —many—of the passages are wise and noble, like those quoted above. Others are fantastic and bewildering and incoherent. Certain books are mere lecture notes, compressed and hard to understand.

Most of the fantastic sections in the Hippocratic writings are probably later additions. Hippocrates was too sensible, too hardheaded, to have given rein to some of the plays of imagination that can be found in the works ascribed to him. The Father of Medicine is one of the most attractive individuals in history. There is a largeness of character about him, a bold strength, that stamps him as unique, that earns him his rank in his profession.

The Hippocratic Oath's final sentence is: "Now if I carry out this oath, and break it not, may I gain forever reputation among all men for my life and for my art; but if I transgress it and forswear myself, may the opposite befall me."

Hippocrates must have abided by his Oath to the end of his days. For he has gained forever reputation among all men for his life and for his art.

2

Galen: The Dead Hand of Tradition

Often it happens that a great man's followers distort and alter his teachings so they give the lie to the teacher's own philosophy. Certainly Christ and Buddha would be surprised if they knew some of the deeds committed by their followers in their names. In the history of medicine, no great doctor has suffered more at the hands of his disciples than Galen.

Galen is considered a Roman doctor, because he lived at a time when Rome ruled the entire civilized world. Actually he was a Greek. He was born in 130 A.D., in the city of Pergamon, Asia Minor. Greek was his native language, and his many books were all written in Greek, though he was living in Rome when he wrote most of them.

Many people tend to think of Galen and Hippocrates as contemporaries. Both lived in ancient times, and it is hard to distinguish one century from another at so great a distance in time. Yet Galen was born almost six hundred years after Hippocrates. He is no more a contemporary of Hippocrates' than Christopher Columbus is of ours.

Galen's native city of Pergamon had a famous temple of Asklepios. It was one of the important centers of pilgrimage in the Roman world, holding much the same position that Lourdes does for Catholics today. Sick people from far and wide came to the temple in Pergamon to be healed. Galen could not help but grow up aware of the importance

28

of the healer's art. He understood both the value and the shortcomings of the followers of Asklepios, with their dependence on prayer and faith.

There was also an established Christian church in Pergamon in Galen's time. But Galen was no Christian. Though a deeply religious man, as we shall see, he remained a pagan. But he respected the teachings of Christ, and said of the members of the new sect, "In their keen pursuit of justice, they are not a whit behind the real philosophers."

Galen's father meant him to be one of those "real philosophers," not a doctor. His father's name was Nikon. Nikon was an architect and an amateur mathematician. He was wealthy and owned a large estate outside the city of Pergamon. Galen was born on that estate. He describes his father as "calm, honorable, and friendly," but says that his mother was "quarrelsome, frequently hit her servants, and quarreled with her husband." He compares her to that famous shrew Xantippe, the wife of Socrates.

Nikon sent young Galen to attend lectures by philosophers of every breed—the followers of Plato, the disciples of Aristotle, those of Epicurus, and the Stoics. Certainly he had an impartial education!

One night, Galen tells us, the god Asklepios came to Nikon in a dream. "Dedicate your son to my service," Asklepios ordered. "He is to be a doctor!"

Nikon obeyed the commandment of the dream unhesitatingly. Like many men of his time, even educated ones, he believed fully in the truth of dreams. So, at seventeen, Galen entered the temple of Asklepios at Pergamon to study medicine with the priests.

Galen welcomed the new career. Philosophy had troubled him because of its uncertainty. One could argue day and night, and never arrive at anything capable of proof. But medicine was different. Medicine rested on facts. Medicine could lead a man to truth.

The Asclepiads, though, had little to teach the boy. Galen moved on to nearby Smyrna after several years and then to Alexandria, the center of the Greek world, where there was a great university and the finest library of antiquity.

Galen spent five years in Alexandria and surrounding parts of Egypt—his twenty-first year through his twenty-sixth. He studied first anatomy, then medicine. As in the time of Hippocrates, it was impossible to dissect human beings to gain an understanding of their bodies. Galen had to be content with dissecting animals, though occasionally he had the opportunity to examine the body of a human being.

He was not enthusiastic about the quality of his teachers, even in famed Alexandria. He wrote, "The art of medicine was taught by ignoramuses in long illogical lectures to crowds of 14-year-old boys who never got near the sick." In Alexandria his own talents asserted themselves, and he must have easily excelled above the "ignoramuses" who were his teachers.

Galen's medical education lasted eleven years, a long time in that era of short lives. At the age of 28, he returned to Pergamon, now a learned physician and anatomist. His native city welcomed him gladly. He had already written several medical books, and his fame had preceded him home.

He was given an appointment as physician to the gladiators of Pergamon. It was his task to repair the professional warriors after they had hacked and slashed at each other for the amusement of the citizens.

This was an important opportunity for Galen. Each week at the gladiatorial games, gladiators dead and gladiators dying were hauled from the field, and in ministering to them Galen had a chance to master the human anatomy. Their wounds and injuries provided him with superb medical experience. He treated the ruptured tendons and nerves of the gladiators, struggled against infection, learned how to sew up slashed abdomens, how to repair battered bodies.

During this time Galen also made an important anatomical discovery. He showed that by cutting the laryngeal nerve of a pig, he could render the animal incapable of squealing. Aristotle had taught that the brain had no connection with sensation or thought. But the laryngeal nerve came from the brain and cutting it caused loss of speech, so Galen had refuted Aristotle and demonstrated the connection between the brain and the voice.

The appointment as physician to the gladiators was for a term of seven months. Galen was appointed four times in all, serving from 158 to 161. He must have kept his gladiators in good health.

In 161, the outbreak of war in Asia Minor put a temporary stop to gladiatorial games. Galen took this opportunity to go to Rome, the capital of the world. The wise emperor Marcus Aurelius had just come to the throne, and Rome was in the full flush of its time of greatest power and glory.

Galen studied, wrote, and lectured in Rome, as well as practiced medicine. He soon was sought by many. His fame spread, and Marcus Aurelius himself employed him as physician to the Emperor.

But Galen paid the penalty for being too successful. He made enemies. Unlike Hippocrates, that calm man of great wisdom and serenity, Galen was often hot-tempered and arrogant. Both were medical geniuses, but while Hippocrates was content to report his failures as well as his triumphs, Galen sometimes tended to be boastful and vain. The doctors of Rome came to dislike this upstart Greek who had ventured into their midst and won such acclaim.

One case in particular earned him their enmity. The physician Eudemos became paralyzed. He could not move the third and fourth fingers of his right hand. Every important doctor in Rome came to examine him. No one knew how to cure the paralysis.

Galen finally was called in. He remembered some experiments he had performed on an ape in Alexandria. He had cut some nerves leading to the ape's spinal cord, and the ape had become paralyzed.

He questioned Eudemos. "Did you injure your back or neck in any way recently?"

Eudemos was puzzled. What did his neck have to do with his paralyzed fingers? But he said, "Yes. I was thrown from a chariot not long ago. I struck my neck against a stone. But I was merely bruised."

"And after that, you could not move your fingers?"

"Yes. But what is the connection?"

Galen treated the nerve in Eudemos' neck, instead of the physician's fingers. Eudemos recovered. Galen's fame climbed to new heights in Rome. But his fellow doctors were more envious than ever. To them, Galen seemed to have almost magical powers of healing—all because he had devoted many years to close study of the body and had some idea of the linkage between injury and ailment, between cause and effect.

There were rumors of a plot against Galen's life. Eudemos himself warned Galen that the other doctors were conspiring to do away with him. He chose the path of prudence, and left Rome, returning to Pergamon.

Emperor Marcus Aurelius, however, was not anxious to lose the great physician's services. He summoned Galen back to Rome, and Galen obeyed. His rivals, realizing he had the protection of the Emperor, kept their grumblings to themselves thenceforth, and Galen spent most of the rest of his life in Rome, as physician to Marcus Aurelius and to the two emperors who succeeded him.

One of Galen's great cases involved Marcus Aurelius. The Emperor developed fever and convulsions while abroad. The doctors who were with him gave him medicines, which only made the fever worse. They felt his pulse, and did all they knew to comfort him, and put him on a liquid diet. All to no avail. The doctors huddled round, each with some different idea of what was wrong. One said it was an attack of malaria; another thought it was a heart attack. They vied with each other in guessing at the Emperor's dread malady.

Galen was summoned. The Emperor meekly held forth his wrist, so Galen might count his pulse as the other doctors had done. But Galen smiled and said, "These other gentlemen have already felt your pulse. Surely they must know its characteristics by now, and they say you have an attack of malaria."

"Feel my pulse anyway," Marcus Aurelius insisted.

Galen did so. It seemed to him not to indicate anything dire, despite the opinions of the other doctors.

Galen said, "You have no serious ailment. Your stomach is overloaded with food." It was a simple attack of indigestion!

The Emperor was pleased with the diagnosis. "That's it," he declared. "It is just what you say. I feel I am weighed down by chilling food."

The other doctors clung to their elaborate and frightening diagnoses. But Galen was confident that he was right. The other doctors prescribed giving the Emperor nourishment, or sending him to the bath.

Galen said, "I would give his majesty some wine with pepper in it, and bandage his stomach with wool dipped in warm ointment."

The remedy was applied. The Emperor recovered.

"After the drink," Galen wrote, "he said to Pitholaus, that there was one physician who was not hidebound by rules, and from this time he never stopped lauding me. He is the First of Physicians, said he, and also of Philosophers. For Marcus had already had experience with many, not only desirous of money, but contentious, vainglorious, envious, and malignant."

Galen was not only a famed doctor but a busy writer. He wrote, according to his own statement, 125 books on philosophy, mathematics, grammar, and law, and an uncounted number of medical treatises. In 192, about ten years before his death, many of Galen's works were lost when fire swept the Temple of Peace, where his manuscripts were stored. Despite this loss, a vast body of writings of Galen has survived to this day. They total 2,500,000 words—equal to fifty books the length of the one you are reading. And there is no doubt that this material was written by Galen himself. The uncertainty that shrouds the Hippocratic Corpus does not extend to Galen's works.

Galen adopted many of Hippocrates' ideas, such as that of the four humors, blood, phlegm. yellow bile, and black bile. Hippocrates was the only doctor besides himself for whom Galen seems to have had genuine respect. Again and again in his works he expresses his admiration for the great teacher of Cos.

Galen believed that much medical truth could be derived by the process of reasoning, as in mathematics. "Geometry," he wrote, "demonstrates its first theorem by *a priori* reasoning, its second from the proof of the first, and thus continues to add one proposition after another, using all of the previously acquired knowledge, until it eventually arrives, incredible as it may seem to the uneducated, not only at the magnitude of the sun, moon, and earth, but at their distances. . . . I decided, therefore, if conclusions in connection with the cure of disease were thus grounded, physicians would manifest an accord like that of the geometricians."

But pure reason was not enough, in medicine. He also wrote, "The proof of correct treatment is based on two criteria, reason and experience. If someone asks why we give cold water to a fever patient we answer for two reasons: First, on account of the nature of fever and the nature of cold water (logical opposites); second, on account of experience, because in this particular disease, under similar circumstances, cold water has been found to be beneficial."

A strong religious theme also runs through Galen's works. The human body in all its miraculous complexity, he believed, was the surest proof of the existence of God. "Every man who looks at things with an open mind, seeing a spirit living in this mass of flesh and humors, and examining the structure of any animal whatever . . . will comprehend the excellence of the spirit which is in heaven."

He was a great experimental physician. He carried out a large number of dissections of animals, and drew conclusions from his findings that were far in advance of his time. Much of what he concluded was wrong, of course. He totally misunderstood the circulation of the blood, and his ideas on human anatomy later proved to be bizarrely incorrect. But the bulk of his work is sound.

He knew, for instance, the functions of the stomach: to receive food, to prepare it for digestion, and to force it into the small intestine. He could distinguish between those nerves that carry sense impressions to the brain, and those that control the movements of the body. His description of the larger muscles of the body was so accurate that it is still used in anatomical textbooks. He had a good knowledge of the skeleton and of the interior of the brain.

The list of Galen's medical accomplishments can be drawn out for hundreds of pages. Compared with Galen, Hippocrates seems innocent and simple, a man groping in the dark. Galen's keen mind sought and found the truth, while Hippocrates, six centuries earlier, could only begin to formulate general principles.

Galen's works are a vast encyclopedia of medicine. No one before him penetrated so deeply into the secrets of the body. Few doctors after him have had such a wide range of understanding of medicine.

He was well aware of his own genius, of course, and this is why we cannot love him as we love Hippocrates. Hippocrates would never have written these lines of Galen's:

"Never yet have I gone astray, whether in treatment or in prognosis, as have so many other physicians of great reputation. If anyone wishes to gain fame . . . all that he needs is to accept what I have been able to establish."

His long years in Rome were active ones. When Marcus Aurelius died in 180, his successor, Commodus, kept Galen on as chief court physician. But the Roman Empire was past its peak and beginning to crumble. Commodus was a brute of a man who enjoyed entering into the gladiatorial games himself, and he met a violent death at the hands of his own courtiers in 193. His successor, Septimus Severus, was equally barbaric, and Galen remained at his court only a few years before deciding to leave the growing disorder of Rome.

In old age, approaching 70, he traveled back through Asia Minor, revisited Pergamon, and then died, about A.D. 200, possibly on the island of Sicily. His final years were spent in writing and meditation. We know little of those years.

An odd thing happened to Galen after his death. He became dictator of all medicine and held sway for fifteen hundred years. His writings became a kind of bible of medicine—and like all holy scriptures, they were regarded as sacred. It was deemed sinful to disagree with Galen. It was like rising up to declare that the Bible itself was fiction.

Galen was a vain and egotistical man, so perhaps he would have been pleased to know that his work became eternally famous. But certainly the man of medicine in him would have been horrified at the way his teachings were distorted and twisted.

Consider these words of Galen's, from his book *On Anatomical Procedure:*

> The human bones are subjects of study with which you should first become perfectly familiar. You cannot merely read about the bones in one of these books which are called by some "Osteology," by others "The Skeleton," and by others simply "On Bones," such as this my own book; which is much more reliable and exact than any previously written on the subject. Pursue by hard study, then, not only the descriptions of the bones in the book, but also acquaint yourself with the appearance of each of the bones, by the use of your own eyes handling each bone by itself so that you become a firsthand observer.

By the use of your own eyes. This was Galen's message—but it went for naught. In the centuries that followed Galen, independent thinking and the use of one's own eyes were frowned upon. To seek for knowledge became a kind of sin. Galen's teachings were all that a doctor needed to know, it was felt.

And so Galen's brilliant work was wasted. His faults and errors were enshrined with his virtues. Medicine in Europe fell victim to the same fate that had befallen it in Egypt, in India, in Babylonia. The stream of discovery was damned. New experiment vanished.

In any body of learning, errors creep in with time. When there are men of understanding around to watch and guard, error can be weeded out. But when error is allowed to flourish, in the name of a sacred and untouchable tradition, its rank growth soon chokes out the tender shoots of truth.

Darkness fell over Europe.

Medicine became a matter of "Galen says this" and "Galen says that." Using one's own mind was sacrilegious. No matter that commonsense argued one thing; Galen's text said another! Medicine dropped back to the mumbojumbo level of thousands of years earlier.

Galen could not have wanted this. Galen had written:

> The doctrines of Hippocrates may be judged as to their truth and exactitude not only from a study of his commentators and opponents, but by going directly to Nature and observing the functions of animals, the subjects of natural research.

Natural research, going directly to Nature—these things became forbidden, and men lost their lives for daring to seek for truth. The very things that Galen had warned against came to pass—and the man who had urged experiment, who had preached against relying on textbooks and commentaries, became himself the supreme authority of medicine, the author of the texts that could not be questioned.

Galen became a dead hand of tradition, stretched across the throat of medicine. Great sins of ignorance were committed in his name. It was a strange and unhappy fate for one of the boldest and most vigorous medical minds of the ages.

3

Vesalius: The Prince of Grave Robbers

FIFTEEN HUNDRED years is a vast span of time. It would be wrong to say that medicine made no progress during the fifteen centuries after Galen's death. Though his words hung heavy over the doctors who followed him, there were always a few who pursued their own paths.

Many of these were Arabs. The Arab physician Ar-Razi, known to the west as "Rhazes," was a beacon in the general darkness. Rhazes, born in 852, studied Galen but wrote his own texts. He often departed far from Galen's teachings.

Half a century after him came another great Arab doctor, Avicenna, known to his contemporaries as "The Prince of Physicians." Mathematician and philosopher as well as man of medicine, Avicenna wrote a huge medical textbook which was still being used at the University of Vienna five hundred years after his death.

In Byzantium, that final outpost of the Roman Empire, other important doctors flourished in the first thousand years after Christ. But in western Europe there was little but darkness. Not till the twelfth and thirteenth centuries did men once again dare to think for themselves, to use their own eyes instead of falling back on sterile dogmas hallowed by time.

One of the men who aided in this rebirth of medicine was Constantine of Africa (1010–1087). He practiced medicine in the Near East before crossing the Mediterranean and coming to Salerno, a town in Italy near Naples. There, he spent his long life translating Arabic medical texts into Latin. This man of two civilizations brought the fruits of the Arabic medical genius to the Christian world.

A school of medicine sprang up at Salerno, and its influence on medicine in the Middle Ages was great. All through Europe, a bubbling ferment of curiosity and scientific zeal came into being.

The bold men of this intellectual revolution were harassed by the Church. Independent thought was a threat to the Church's authority. Some, like the thirteenth-century Italian doctor Pietro D'Abando, were tried by the Inquisition on charges of "sorcery, heresy, and necromancy."

Pietro died before he could be convicted, but the Inquisitors burned his body. A doctor in those superstitious days could not afford to be too successful at the healing arts, for fear of being thought in league with Satan.

One who survived the risks of success was the Frenchman Guy de Chauliac (1300–1368) who was chief surgeon to the Popes during their exile at Avignon, France. Guy used anesthetic drugs when he operated and believed in the use of healing salves and plasters to prevent infection—unlike many of his colleagues, who felt that nature should be allowed to take her course. He performed successful hernia operations, treated cataracts of the eye, and removed cancerous growths by cauterizing them. Like all surgeons of that violent era, he was an expert on arrow wounds and spear wounds. This is a sample of Guy's surgical thinking:

> The method of operating which suits particular cases is such that if the infixed body cannot conveniently be extracted at the first attempt, it ought to be left alone until the flesh withers or corrupts and then by twisting it and moving it here and there the infixed body will be more easily drawn out, notwithstanding the

dictum of Henric, who orders that they be extracted immediately because Avicenna, Albucasis and Brunus so wished.

Then the wound should be cared for just like others, except that the blood altered by the infixed body must be expressed so that the wound may be assured against putrefaction; and warm oil must be poured into it, especially if there is question of pain.

Notice how unimpressed Guy is with established medical authorities of the past such as Avicenna! A fresh breeze was blowing in the fourteenth century. Note, too, his urgent concern with avoiding infection and gangrene.

Men of this sort boldly pushed back the borders of ignorance and brought light to dark areas of medicine. But one big obstacle was the lack of any detailed and systematic understanding of human anatomy. It had always been considered evil to dissect human corpses. In the time of Guy de Chauliac, Pope Boniface VIII expressly forbade such dissections. Surgeons had to learn their trade by dissecting animals. They could cut up a human cadaver only at the risk of their lives.

Few doctors would run that risk. They preferred to depend on Galen's anatomical teachings. But Galen had made many mistakes of observation. And Galen's later followers had added new errors of their own, encrusting his work with superstition and confusion.

For instance, the Bible tells us that God created woman by drawing a rib from Adam's side. Therefore, the official medical authorities of the Middle Ages decided that men must have one less rib than women!

Any doctor who privately counted ribs, and discovered that the number was the same in both sexes, would be denounced as a subversive, a heretic, if he spoke out. And there were other strange ideas in force about the shape of the liver, the breastbone, the uterus, and most of the rest of the body. Naturally, with anatomy in such a primitive state, any doctor who attempted surgery would have done little worse had he operated with his eyes closed.

Then the Renaissance swept over Europe—the rebirth of knowledge, tearing away the cobwebs of ignorance.

In Italy, a new school of painters appeared. They wanted to paint the human body as it really was, instead of using the traditional stiff, unnatural stylistic conventions. That meant studying anatomy. Such artists as Leonardo da Vinci privately studied anatomy and made firsthand observations. They discovered that the standard medical teachings about the body were wrong. But they were only painters, after all. Did a painter dare to lecture to doctors on anatomy?

A few physicians were beginning to question the hitherto sacred word of Galen, though. Although it was forbidden to dissect most corpses, it became customary to allow the bodies of executed criminals to be used for the study of anatomy. Each medical school was permitted to hold two or three public dissections of criminals each year. Students came from afar to attend these dissections.

Even so, doctors would not accept the evidence of their eyes. When experiment showed one thing and Galen taught another, they told themselves that they had obviously made some mistake in observation.

If Galen taught that the liver had five lobes, and dissection produced a liver that failed to follow Galen's description—well, either the corpse just dissected had been abnormal, or else the human body must have changed since Galen's time. Few physicians had the strength to rise up and declare flatly, "Galen was wrong. We can see for ourselves that the liver does not have five lobes!"

A man born in 1514 did much to end the supremacy of Galen's anatomical teachings. He was Andreas Vesalius, Brussels-born, son of an apothecary, grandson and great-grandson of physicians. If Avicenna was the Prince of Physicians, Vesalius must be called the Prince of Grave Robbers, since that is how he obtained his specimens for dissection. But another title is his beyond question—King of Anatomists.

As a boy, young Andreas was forever trying to see what lay beneath the skins of animals. Any hapless beast that came his way—

cat, dog, rabbit, toad—fell victim to his curiosity. The interplay between muscle and bone, the mysteries of the body, these things fascinated him. He toiled for hours over his dissections. Even in childhood his methods were startlingly precise, his observations amazingly keen.

His family recognized his abilities, and gave him a good education. They sent him to Louvain for his preliminary instruction, then on to Paris at the age of 17 to begin his medical studies. He grew up quick-witted, tough-minded, a strong, stocky young man. He was stubborn and self-willed, and seemed destined for greatness—and trouble.

His teacher in Paris was Jacobus Sylvius, one of the great doctors of his day, whose medical classes were attended by as many as 400 young men. Sylvius occasionally used human cadavers to illustrate his anatomy lectures. But he was a conservative man. He was of the "Galen-was-right" school. Sylvius taught that the liver was five-lobed, that the breastbone had seven segments, that man had one less rib than woman.

This was plainly nonsense to Vesalius. More than once, Dr. Sylvius had let the young man actually take part in the dissections. Vesalius had handled the scalpels, he had seen the liver for himself, he had counted the ribs. How could the doctors see one thing and teach another?

"Perhaps I did not see correctly," Vesalius told himself.

And so—to add to the information he had gained from Sylvius' infrequent dissections—Vesalius began slipping into graveyards by night and going to places of execution where dead men were left swinging on gibbets. There, by torchlight, and under conditions that must have been terrifying in that age of superstition, Vesalius performed his own private dissections.

He confirmed all that he had seen. Sylvius was teaching twaddle. Galen was wrong.

Galen was wrong!

Cocky and confident, Vesalius did not hesitate even to humiliate Sylvius in his own classroom. One day, dissecting a dog, Sylvius searched in vain for the valves of the heart. He groped through the bloody corpse for long minutes without success. Finally he declared, "These valves are mentioned by Galen. Therefore they exist. The dog must be incorrectly constructed!"

"Imagine that," snorted Vesalius, half out loud. "A mere dog dares to contradict the great Galen!"

Sylvius looked up, startled by the outburst. "What was that comment, young man?"

Vesalius repeated it. Then, growing even more bold, he stepped to the front of the lecture hall. Taking the instruments from the flabbergasted Sylvius, Vesalius deftly laid bare the elusive valves. "They are here after all, it would seem."

"Cleverly done," Sylvius sputtered. "Cleverly done, young man!" But he was mortally wounded. He would never forget how Vesalius had publicly mocked him.

Vesalius was more convinced than ever that Sylvius and the others were teaching a distortion of Galen. Had Galen himself not written, "I would ask you to make yourself acquainted with human bones. . . . I have often had the chance to do this where tombs or monuments have been broken up"?

Clearly it was not Galen but the men who taught his ideas who were at fault. Galen himself certainly would not have approved of the way his errors had been frozen into dogma.

So Vesalius continued his clandestine midnight work at the gibbets, in the cemeteries. Had he been caught, his own corpse would have dangled from a gibbet soon enough!

War forced him to leave Paris. He returned to Louvain, where he received his degree in 1537. At Louvain, he secretly acquired a nearly complete human skeleton, lacking only a foot, a finger, and a kneecap. It was the skeleton of a man who had been executed and whose flesh had been picked by the birds. Vesalius carried off this trophy and mounted it.

After taking his degree, Vesalius moved on to the University of Padua, a great scientific center, and at the age of 23 became professor of surgery and anatomy there. He lectured twice daily and held public dissections as often as he could persuade the town authorities to let him have the bodies of executed criminals. Since most criminals were men, Vesalius had little opportunity to study the female anatomy. He dissected only six female cadavers in his whole career and for this reason was often in error on matters of female structure.

He flourished in Padua. His brilliance and demonic energy, his stout self-confidence, above all his fearlessness, made him one of the most esteemed medical lecturers in Europe, despite his youth.

In 1538 a famous publishing house hired him to edit a new edition of Galen's anatomical writings. Vesalius was still in awe of Galen's reputation, and so he was greatly puzzled by the host of obvious mistakes in Galen's anatomical teachings.

Then Vesalius made a major discovery. He obtained the skeleton of a monkey and found that it conformed to Galen's anatomical ideas. Now he understood! Galen had based his anatomy only on the dissection of lower animals! He had not really observed human cadavers! No wonder he was full of errors—and how foolish it had been to turn those errors into holy writ!

"I could not get over my own stupidity and overconfidence in Galen and other anatomists," Vesalius wrote. Freed now of any need to rely on Galen's teachings, he publicly declared that he had found more than two hundred errors in Galen.

Wild controversy and fierce disputes followed. Young men rallied around Vesalius and his "subversive" ideas. Older, more conservative teachers denounced him violently. But he weathered the storm. He had an ambitious plan now: to publish his own book on anatomy. It would be a masterpiece, a monument of scientific research.

He worked on it for three years. He completed it in August, 1542, when he was only 27. It was published the following year by a celebrated firm in Switzerland. The illustrations were done by Vesalius' friend and colleague, Jan van Calcar, and the engraved plates had to be shipped from Padua to Basel by muleback, over the Alps, a hazardous three-week journey. Of this trip the surgeon and biographer

Harvey Cushing has written, "The misstep of a single donkey on the high passes, known to be in a state of great disrepair, might thwart all his labors of the preceding three years."

The mules arrived safely. In June, 1543, Vesalius' epochal book, *De Humani Corporis Fabrica* ("On the Fabric of the Human Body") was published. It was a magnificent volume of 663 large pages, with over 300 breathtaking illustrations of the human body.

The *Fabrica* is one of the classics of medicine. It is divided into seven books: on the skeleton, the muscles, the blood vessels, the nervous system, the abdominal viscera, the thoracic viscera, and the brain. Hundreds of Galen's errors were swept away—the missing male rib, the five-lobed liver, the segmented breastbone, and much else.

Vesalius worked out the action of each muscle, had a good description of the heart, traced many of the important nerves. Naturally, there were numerous new errors. His idea of the internal anatomy of the eye was vague, his description of the female reproductive system was extremely poor, and there were some mistakes on the smaller bones and nerves. But for its time the book was a mighty accomplishment of clear-eyed observation, the first of its kind since Galen himself had examined cadavers in the remote past.

Vesalius was just 28 when it was published. His fame was assured. From then on, his life was a downhill slide, with no other great accomplishments.

In the introduction to the *Fabrica,* Vesalius spoke of surgeons and medical professors who "Indeed, from a lofty chair arrogantly cackle like jackdaws about things which they never have tried, but which they commit to memory from the books of others or which they place in written form before their eyes." Speaking of the medical schools of his day, Vesalius said acidly, "And thus all things are taught wrongly, and days go by in silly disputations. Fewer facts are placed before the spectators in that tumult than a butcher could teach a doctor in his meat market. I shall not mention those schools where they hardly ever think of dissecting the structure of the human body, with the result that ancient medicine declined from its pristine glory years ago."

He minced no words for the disciples of Galen. "The principal followers of Galen put their trust in some kind of talking, and relying upon the inertia of others in dissecting, they shamelessly abridge Galen into elaborate compendia. They do not depart from him a hair's breadth while they are following his sense; but to the front of their books they add writings of their own, stitched together completely from the opinions of Galen—and all of theirs is from him. The whole lot of them have placed their faith in him, with the result that you can not find a doctor who has thought that even the slightest slip has ever been detected in the anatomical volumes of Galen, much less *could* be found (now)."

Doctors then as today are easily stung by sarcasm. They quickly retort hotly to any attacks by young whippersnappers. This bold, slashing onslaught by an upstart like Vesalius brought immediate counterattacks.

He was denounced all over Europe. One of his most vehement enemies was Sylvius, his old teacher, who launched an unbelievable campaign of mudslinging. The old order was fighting for its life.

Every small error of Vesalius' was pounced on and magnified. His attacks on Galen were regarded as near heresy. Wherever he turned, he found enemies, plotters, conspirators. Sylvius still had great influence. Vesalius was forced to leave Padua after the *Fabrica* was published.

The Emperor Charles V invited him to come to Spain and be his court physician. Vesalius accepted. In despair, he burned the manuscript of a second book he had been working on and withdrew from further research. He frittered away years in useless attempts to defend himself and wandered through Europe in the train of the restless emperor. His career as a trailblazer of science was over. He became a controversial and weary figure whose greatness was behind him. Though he had once said that a man who would woo science should never take a wife, he married now—an indication that he regarded his scientific career as ended.

We know little of his dismal later years. In 1564 he was on his way to the Holy Land in pilgrimage. Why? No one knows. There is a letter which, written soon after his death, gives one theory:

They say that Vesalius is dead. Doubtless you have heard he went to Jerusalem. That journey had, as they tell us from Spain, an odd reason. Vesalius, believing a young Spanish nobleman whom he had attended to be dead, obtained leave of the parents to open the body, for the sake of inquiring into the cause of the illness, which he had not rightly comprehended; but he had no sooner made an incision into the body than he perceived the symptoms of life, and opening the breast saw the heart beat. The parents, coming afterward to the knowledge of this, were not satisfied with prosecuting for murder, but accused him to the Inquisition of impiety, in hopes that he would be punished with greater vigor by the judges of that tribunal than by those of the common law. But the king of Spain interposed and saved him on condition that by way of atoning for the error he should undertake a journey to the Holy Land.

Perhaps. Whatever the reason, he visited Jerusalem, and on the way back died on the island of Zante in the Aegean Sea, possibly in a shipwreck, possibly of the plague. He was not quite 50 years old, and his great accomplishment—the publication of the *Fabrica*—had come 21 years before.

Vesalius' boldness in attacking Galen turned his life into a tragedy of bitterness and failure. Like Copernicus, like Galileo, like all those who fought against dogma and ignorance, he was blocked, denounced, scorned, and hated.

But the *Fabrica* stands as Vesalius' monument, and no man will ever need a finer one. This massive book cuts like a scalpel through the shroud of ignorance and confusion that had bound medicine in the Middle Ages.

In time the achievement of Vesalius attained the recognition it deserved. Superstition and fear gave way. In 1556, while Vesalius still lived, the Church reconsidered the old decree of Boniface VIII and declared that it had never been sinful to dissect bodies for medical purposes. Boniface had denounced the "boiling of bones," meaning the custom of gathering the bones of dead crusaders and selling them as relics. After 1556 the Church no longer opposed dissection, and every medical school gave regular anatomy dissections with human cadavers.

Today, freshman medical students work on cadavers as a matter of course. It is a striking contrast to the days when Andreas Vesalius was forced to skulk by torchlight in graveyards and places of execution to search out the secrets of the human body. His work is the foundation on which the modern knowledge of anatomy is based. He is a mighty figure in the story of medicine.

4

Paré: "I Dressed Him and God Healed Him"

THE YEAR is 1552. A young French soldier lies groaning on the battlefield at Danvilliers. Blood spurts from his left leg, hopelessly shattered by an enemy bullet.

A French surgeon kneels over the wounded officer. The surgeon's name is Ambroise Paré, and he is a kind and gentle man whose heart is filled with sadness, for he knows what must be done. He touches the wounded man's feverish forehead.

"The worst will soon be past," Paré tells the young man. "Try to rest."

Behind the surgeon, the French commander, Rohan, stares bleakly at the man on the ground. "Must the leg come off?" Rohan asks quietly.

Paré nods. "Yes. It must. But perhaps I can spare him some torment."

The surgeon has no choice but to remove the leg. It is shattered beyond hope of repair, and unless it is amputated at once, infection and gangrene would set in. Amputation is a dangerous procedure, but it is far safer than allowing the limb to fester, which would mean certain death.

An amputation in the year 1552 is not a pleasant task either for surgeon or for patient. There are no anesthetics; the patient must remain conscious throughout the operation, unless the pain mercifully causes him to faint. And after the amputation comes something even worse: the cautery. Surgeons in the sixteenth century know only one way to prevent the stump from bleeding and that is by cauterization— either applying red-hot irons to the stump or dipping it in a pot of boiling oil.

Paré has no love for the technique of cauterization. He knows that it is excruciatingly painful, and rarely effective, since after a few days the scab would usually open, bleeding would begin again, and the whole process would have to be repeated. For that reason, an amputation is almost certainly a sentence of death, rapid or lingering.

Two young surgeons bring Paré his instruments. Paré sees the fear in the wounded man's eyes, and tries to calm him with a smile, with a touch of the hand. Paré takes the knife and makes his first incision in the leg. Minutes later, he is sawing through the bone, while the wounded young officer holds himself under rigid control and battles to keep from screaming.

The amputation is quickly done. There is never any time to waste, since the pain is hellish, and a man can die of the pain alone. Surgeons have to be speedy. Paré needs no more than three minutes to remove the leg.

One of his assistants, meanwhile, has been heating an iron cautery. Now, with blood spouting from the fresh stump, the assistant begins to hand the cautery to Paré.

Paré shakes his head. "No," he says. "I will not use it this time."

The assistant blinks in confusion. "But how—?"

Paré smiles. "There is something I have long wished to try," he says. "This is the time."

He reaches for his medical kit. He takes some lengths of silk thread from it.

Paré has been reading Galen. He has come across mention of a surgical technique practiced by the ancient doctor but discarded by Galen's dogmatic heirs. It is the tying off, or ligation, of blood vessels. No one has practiced ligation for a thousand years or more. But it seems far more humane than the cautery, and now Paré has found the courage to try it on a wounded man.

Working rapidly, Paré locates the blood vessels of the stump and secures them with forceps. Then he carefully ligates them, tying silk threads about their ends to close them off. When he steps back, finally, his hands are shaking with tension, his face is bathed with perspiration. But the stump no longer bleeds.

"Let the cautery cool," he tells his assistant. "We will not need it now."

The operation is over. Paré later writes of it, "I returned to Paris with my gentleman whose leg I had cut off. I dressed him and God healed him. I sent him to his house, merry, with a wooden leg, and he was content, saying that he had got off cheap not to have been miserably burned to stop the blood."

I dressed him and God healed him. This phrase appears again and again in the memoirs of this great and good doctor of the sixteenth century. He worked a one-man revolution that took much of the cruelty from the practice of surgery.

In the Middle Ages, surgery was practiced not only by skilled doctors but by barbers as well. Wandering surgeons roamed from town to town like tinkers and locksmiths, offering their services here and there. They slashed away merrily, varying the use of the knife with that of cautery by hot iron or boiling oil. These barber-surgeons spilled vast quantities of their patients' blood, so that even today the symbol of a barber is a pole striped with red—for blood—and white— for bandages.

Such anesthetics as existed were used only on the well-to-do. Most patients were simply strapped to their beds and allowed to scream until consciousness left them. Agatha Young, in her book *Scalpel,* provides us with this chilling description of a hospital of the Middle Ages:

> The hospitals of the time were run as institutions of charity by religious orders. They were places of horror. The wards were

filled with great canopied beds placed as close together as possible, and patients were crowded into the darkness of these great cavelike structures, three, sometimes four to a single bed. Sometimes these miserable humans were all laid out in one direction; sometimes with feet and heads alternating. Usually the sexes were not kept separate.

Surgical cases were put in with medical cases, with little regard to whether the disease might be contagious, except in the case of plague, which was universally recognized and feared. Plague patients were not wanted in hospitals; if they appeared, they were bundled off to special pesthouses and largely left to fend for themselves. There was no real comprehension of the connection between dirt and disease, and the sheets of these great beds, when indeed there were any, were thick with blood and pus and grime. Lice swarmed in the bedding, carrying disease from patient to patient, and it is not surprising that epidemics within these hospitals were not uncommon.

The hospital buildings were dirty, ill-lit, usually damp, sometimes cold in winter, sometimes steaming with the heat of sick bodies and chimneyless charcoal braziers. Sewage facilities usually consisted of a hole in the floor at one end of the ward, into which slops and refuse were dumped to drain into the river. . . . The stench which rose into the wards from these sewage holes can scarcely be imagined.

Under these conditions, even the most brilliant of surgeons would lose most of his patients. No matter how skilfully an operation might be carried out, infection or contagion would be almost certain to carry the patient off. Small wonder that the droning of Last Rites, the tolling of the death-bell, could constantly be heard in the hospital.

One of the first surgeons to ponder the problem of control of infection was the fourteenth-century doctor, Guy de Chauliac, as we have seen. But in his day surgery itself was still too primitive to allow the patient much hope of survival. Two centuries later, Vesalius gave surgeons a fuller understanding of human anatomy than they had ever had before, and surgical technique vastly improved. It was now possible to start dealing with matters of sanitation, bleeding, and control of pain.

The great surgeon of Vesalius' day was, like Guy de Chauliac, French. He was Ambroise Paré (1510–1590), a skilled healer, an unusual human being. Born of poor family, he had only a modest education, and failed to learn Latin and Greek, the languages of scholarship and of medicine. "For it did not please God to favor my youth with instruction in one or the other language," Paré said in the preface of a handbook of anatomy he wrote, in French, for the benefit of those who likewise had no classical education.

In boyhood he was apprenticed to a barber-surgeon, who performed minor operations as well as shaves and haircuts. Enthralled by the practice of surgery, young Paré left the provinces and journeyed to Paris. Lacking Latin, he could not enter formal medical studies, but his practical experience as a barber and a surgeon gained him employment at the Hôtel-Dieu, a squalid, disease-ridden hospital on the banks of the Seine. Paré spent three years there.

His medical education was skimpy. Medical texts, being in Latin, were closed books to him, so he was forced to gather his knowledge the hard way, by observation and practice. Life was cheap at the Hôtel-Dieu, and no one minded very much if an apprentice surgeon made an occasional fatal mistake while learning his trade.

In 1536 war broke out between France and the Holy Roman Empire. Paré went to the battlefield as the regimental surgeon to a Marshal Montejan. His chief duty was to care for Montejan—and perhaps to shave him as well as minister to his illnesses and wounds—but he was allowed to treat other soldiers as time permitted. The men were supposed to pay him themselves for his services, as much or as little as they could afford and as they thought he was worth. Paré was 27 at this time.

The army was something of a rag-tag outfit, hastily assembled and poorly trained. It saw active fighting and there were many wounded men. Paré was kept busy caring for the wounded.

Most of the victims had gunshot wounds, for the age of the sword was passing. The early rifles and pistols were highly inaccurate weapons. They had to be discharged point-blank at close range, and so each wound was usually accompanied by powder burns.

The most important European surgeon of the day, Giovanni de Vigo, surgeon to the Pope, taught that powder burns were poisonous and would be fatal unless treated at once. Vigo's "treatment" was a brutal one. It involved spreading the edges of the wound and pouring in boiling oil. This was not only severely painful, but usually made the wound worse instead of better.

Paré was young and inexperienced, and so he conscientiously followed Vigo's treatment. Who was he to differ with the surgeon to the Pope?

But he had qualms about pouring boiling oil into wounds. He wrote, "I knew that caustics could not be poured into wounds without excessive pain. I, before I would run a hazard, determined to see whether the surgeons who went with me in the army used any other manner of dressing to these wounds."

He observed the other surgeons and saw them all busily pouring boiling oil into gunshot wounds, as Vigo recommended. Satisfied that this was the standard treatment, Paré proceeded to do the same.

But as the battle continued, Paré ran out of oil. He was too scrupulous to leave the wounds untreated. Feeling that he had to do something, he concocted a dressing out of egg yolk, oil of roses, and turpentine, and dressed the wounds with that.

All night long he tossed sleeplessly, worrying about the men he had subjected to his improvised treatment. He felt the guilt of a murderer. In the morning he went tensely to see his patients, expecting to find them all dead of the "poisoning" of the gunpowder.

To his great surprise, they were all alive and doing well, and feeling little pain. Their wounds were clean and not inflamed. "The others," he wrote, "those whose wounds had been treated with boiling elder oil, were in high fever, while their wounds were inflamed, swollen, and acutely painful. I determined, therefore, that I would no longer cauterize the unfortunate wounded in so cruel a manner."

The young surgeon had put an end to Vigo's boiling oil treatment. Luck had been with him—for, had he not run out of oil, he might never have tried his own remedy. Paré soon abandoned his improvised salve for another recipe that indicates how much in the dark he really was about medicines:

> *2 newborn puppies*
> *1 pound earthworms*
> *2 pounds oil of lilies*
> *16 ounces Venice turpentine*
> *1 ounce aqua vitae*
> *Boil the puppies (alive) in the oil. Add the worms, which have been drowned in white wine. Boil and strain. Add the other ingredients.*

This shows that Paré was far from being free from the medical fantasies of the Middle Ages. But at least the boiling-oil remedy had been abandoned. Paré's earthworm salve may not have promoted healing, but at least it did no damage of its own, unlike the boiling oil.

Paré attracted favorable attention during this campaign. An Italian doctor remarked to Marshal Montejan, "Sir, you have with you a surgeon who, though young in years, is old in knowledge and experience. Take great care of him, for he will do you good service and bring you honor."

The soldiers, too, were fond of the gentle young surgeon who was so eager to spare them from pain. They filled a helmet with coins to reward him. It was the custom among them to slit the throats of the badly wounded to end their miseries, but Paré forbade this and worked diligently to save every patient. He became greatly beloved, and his fame spread.

The war ended in 1538. Paré returnd to Paris and visited Jacobus Sylvius—the same Sylvius who would later cause so much trouble for

Vesalius. Paré told Sylvius how he had disproved Vigo's teachings. You might think that Sylvius, the conservative, would criticize **Paré** for challenging his masters. But, surprisingly, Sylvius was interested in the young man's ideas. Since there was nothing in Galen about gunshot wounds, Sylvius felt free to accept this new notion, and he embraced Paré's beliefs.

But Paré was as gentle and retiring a man as Vesalius was a stubborn and persistent one. Paré's ideas of sparing the patient pain were slow to spread. He went into private practice and wrote a book on the treatment of gunshot wounds which was not published until 1545. Four years later, when he published his French-language text in anatomy, he was brave enough to accept the new teachings of Vesalius.

War broke out again in 1552 and again Paré went to the battlefield. Using healing salves instead of boiling oil, he saved many men from death—though he was always careful to note, in his case histories, "I dressed him and God healed him."

It was on this campaign that he turned his attention to the problem of battlefield amputations. He made his famous experiments with ligation. With typical caution, he kept a heated iron handy in case the method did not work and cautery was needed.

But it did work. Ligation proved to be in every way superior to cautery in amputation cases. Even though Paré had the weight of Galen's authority on his side, he could not get his fellow doctors to accept ligation at once. As he wrote years later, his rivals believed that since "to tie the vessel after amputation is a new remedy . . . therefore it should not be used."

Paré returned to Paris in 1554, and in recognition of his extraordinary services at the battlefield, he was granted a signal honor. Although he did not have a formal education, and had never taken a medical degree, he was given the rank of master surgeon. He no longer had to call himself a barber.

He became surgeon to King Henri II, and in the years that followed was witness to royal intrigue and court skulduggery. Henri died in

1559, wounded by a lance in a tournament. Paré was unable to save him, even though another famous doctor, none other than Andreas Vesalius, was called in to consult on the case. Paré became surgeon to Henri's successor, the short-lived boy-king, François II. When the sickly François died, eighteen months later, Paré's enemies—great doctors invariably draw malicious enemies—whispered that Paré had poured poison in the King's ear. Paré survived the rumor, and the new King, Charles IX, not only kept him on as surgeon, but in 1562 gave him the dignified title, First Surgeon of the King.

Through years of civil war, assassinations, and religious strife, Paré remained as far from politics as he could stay. He devoted himself to the healing arts, and accomplished important reforms in surgical practice, obstetrics, and hospital procedure.

When he was 65, he turned once again to writing, and published his collected works, including his memoirs. They are among the most charming of medical autobiographies, for Paré was not only a good and saintly man, but a delightful writer as well. His books contain much valuable surgical advice, but they are not free of the superstitions of the day, such as the thought that the touch of a king's hand could cure certain diseases.

Charming as Paré's books were, they aroused enmity among some of the conservatives in the medical schools. One of these enemies was a Dr. Gourmelen who had long brooded over Paré's fame. Gourmelen had once criticized Paré's ligation technique as "a new way of tying the vessels, against the opinion of all the ancients." In his reply, Paré had exposed Gourmelen's ignorance by declaring that ligation was described and recommended in the works of Hippocrates, Galen, Avicenna, and Guy de Chauliac, among others.

Now Gourmelen did his best to get Paré's collected works suppressed. He lodged charges of plagiarism and corruption of morals against Paré, invoking an old decree that prohibited the publication of medical books that did not bear the approval of the medical faculty of Paris.

Paré was vindicated. His books were approved and went into four editions in his own lifetime, dozens afterwards. Paré told Gourmelen triumphantly, "Now will you say you will teach me how to perform works of surgery, you who have never yet come out of your study? . . . The operations of surgery are learned by the eye and by the hand."

Paré lived to a great old age, like Hippocrates and Galen before him. He practiced medicine to the last, never losing his concern for those who suffered. In 1590, he died in his 80th year, full of honors.

Ambroise Paré was a profoundly humane man, and out of this humanitarian concern of his came his great surgical discoveries. Not a scholar nor a lover of tradition for its own sake, he worked humbly, accepting the evidence of his eyes, using trial and error, and guiding himself always by the desire to heal and to reduce the pain of the sufferer.

His importance is a double one. First, he made major technical strides, such as his introduction of ligation and his treatment of gunshot wounds. Secondly, his philosophy of medicine, his humility and freedom from constricting dogma, mark his achievement. Many surgeons of his time failed to remember that they were working on human beings. They slashed and hacked away with no regard for the pain they were causing. Paré felt otherwise. There is nobility in his simple devotion to his patients.

A great historian of medicine, Henry Sigerist, wrote this of Ambroise Paré:

> He was extremely modest, this modesty being the outcome of a profound piety which was untinged by bigotry. For him . . . the foundation of the healing art must be love. Again and again we find him adjuring young surgeons not to work for the sake of monetary reward, and to do their duty to the last even in hopeless cases or cases that appeared hopeless. "For nature often brings things to pass which seem impossible to the surgeon." If the surgeon was successful in bringing about a cure, he must not

plume himself on this, but must ascribe the happy result to God's grace.

Ambroise Paré's own words are his finest epitaph:

I dressed him and God healed him.

5

Harvey: The Motion of the Heart

Oₙₑ of the few facts we know about Hippocrates is that he
was short of stature. One of the things we know about Galen is that
he was short of temper.

Now comes a man who is both short of stature and short of temper.
And he shares a third characteristic with both Hippocrates and Galen:
He is one of the greatest doctors that ever lived. He is an Englishman,
named William Harvey, who lived from 1578 to 1657.

He pierced the mystery of the human heart.

The seventeenth century was a time when a renewed and ever more
vigorous assault on the mysteries of the universe was made. Galileo
plumbed the heavens with his telescope; Shakespeare probed the human heart through literature; Leeuwenhoeck perfected the microscope and peered in wonder at a world of infinitely small beings.

The mystery of the human body, the living human body, still remained unsolved. Vesalius and his followers had cleared away much of
the confusion, but they had worked only on dead men. The complex
functioning of the living body was still beyond comprehension.

Chief among these mysteries was the circulation of the blood. Blood
vessels had been known for centuries, of course, and ligation and
tourniquets were in common use, but without any real understanding

60

of what was being done. Bold advances in surgery were being made, but until the blood circulation could be understood, no true progress could develop.

Vesalius' followers at Padua had devoted themselves to the problem. One of them, Realdo Colombo, managed to show that the blood flows out of the heart to the lungs, and back through the lungs into the heart. Michael Servetus, a great Spanish anatomist, had earlier made the same discovery, before being burned at the stake for heresy by the fanatic John Calvin in 1553.

Colombo's successor at Padua, Fallopio, went on to amplify Colombo's work. (Fallopio was also the discoverer of the Fallopian tubes in the female reproductive system.) And *his* successor, who bore the resounding name of Girolamo Fabrizio d'Acquapendente, went on to discover the valves of the veins.

But all these men were working in the dark. They had only the haziest notion of the system that the blood vessels comprised. Some doctors felt that the blood moved at random through the veins and arteries. Others held that some mysterious "tide" propelled it. Observation showed that some blood was bright red, and left the body in spurts, while other blood was dark-hued, and ebbed out sluggishly from a punctured vessel. The conclusion was that there were two kinds of blood, and fanciful theories explained the different functions of these two bloods.

The man who put an end to this confusion forever was William Harvey, the greatest figure in English medicine, and one of the most important in the whole history of experimental science. He was the son of a prosperous merchant, who sent him to Cambridge at 16 to study. From there, in 1598, Harvey went on to the famous University at Padua.

John Aubrey, who wrote a book of biographies that gives us a capsule view of almost every great figure of Elizabethan England, has this to say about Harvey. Describing him as "very choleric," or hot-tempered, Aubrey remarks that "in his younger days he would be apt to draw out his dagger upon every light occasion. He was not tall, but of the lowest stature; round-faced . . . ; little eye, round, very black; full of spirit; his hair was black as a raven, but quite white 20 years before he died."

Slim, tense, reserved, the dynamic Harvey swiftly made his imprint at Padua. He became the favorite student of the famed Fabrizio d'Acquapendente, he who had discovered the valves of the veins.

Fabrizio befriended the edgy, ambitious young Englishman, and soon had him inflamed with the desire to understand the workings of that complex network of tubes and pipes we all carry within us. Harvey soon saw that Fabrizio by no means understood his own discoveries. Fabrizio pointed out the valves, or "little doors," of the veins.

"What purpose do they serve?" Fabrizio wondered.

Galen had said the veins carried blood *out* to the limbs. But these little valves seemed to prevent blood from flowing outward through the veins! Fabrizio's confusion was obvious.

"The little doors keep the blood from flowing out too rapidly," Fabrizio concluded lamely.

Harvey was troubled by this explanation. It did not seem to fit the facts. But he could offer no better answer. Galen's ideas on the veins still held sway, since no one had experimentally disproved them.

In April, 1602, Harvey received his degree at Padua, and he returned to London to go into medical practice. He soon was recognized as the outstanding doctor of his day, and by 1609, when he was only 31, "Mr. Doctor Harvey," as he was known, held the post of chief physician to St. Bartholomew's Hospital.

But, though he dutifully carried out his hospital work, his real interest and dedication lay elsewhere. His mind was occupied by the subject that had obsessed him since he had first heard Fabrizio d'Acquapendente lecture—solving the mystery of the circulation of the blood.

He worked in secrecy. He studied animals, dissected them, meditated on his findings. For long hours he pored over his specimens. He opened the bodies of small animals and watched their still-beating hearts, trying to fathom the action. His eyes, quick though they were, could not follow it. In despair he was, as he wrote, "almost tempted to think . . . that the motion of the heart was only to be comprehended by God."

The established theories of the day went back fifteen centuries, to Galen. Galen had taught that the source of the blood is the liver; it flows out into the body, moves about in the blood vessels, passes into the right side of the heart, seeps through into the left, and continues outward. The blood, Galen held, was the carrier of "spiritus," the spirit of life. Air from the lungs filtered into the heart to cool and refresh the blood in its passage.

It was a good enough theory in its time, and no one had ever disproved it entirely. That troublemaker Vesalius had looked at human hearts and had not found any possible way for the blood to get from the right side to the left as Galen said it did. He wrote sarcastically that he wondered "at the handwork of the Almighty, by means of which the blood sweats from the right into the left ventricle through passages which escape human vision."

But Vesalius offered no ideas of his own, nor did those anatomists who followed after him. Galen's teachings were in error, but for lack of any replacement, they remained in acceptance.

By 1615, Harvey had dissected some eighty species of animals and had reached his first general conclusion: The function of the heart was the same in every species, even though the structure was not. Simple animals had simple hearts, complex ones, complex hearts. In cold-blooded creatures like frogs and snakes, the heart moved more slowly than in mammals, and he could follow its motions. He found that the heart was a muscle, whose contractions provided a pumplike action. Each of its quick, jerky convulsions sent blood outward through the arteries. The veins returned it to the heart.

In 1616 Harvey first ventured to tell the world his ideas. He was invited to deliver a series of lectures to the College of Physicians in London. He spoke on surgery and anatomy, and described the circulation of the blood as he understood it.

Those lectures were never published. But Harvey's own notes were preserved. Written in a mixture of English and bad Latin, scribbled in an almost indecipherable hand, they include these historic words:

> William Harvey demonstrates by the structure of the heart that the blood is constantly passed through the lungs into the aorta. . . . He demonstrates by the ligature the passage of blood from arteries to veins. Thus is proved a perpetual motion of the blood *in a circle* caused by the beating of the heart.

The revelation did not result in blaring headlines in the newspapers of the day. In fact, hardly anyone took notice of it, and those who did wrote it off as some fantastic idea that Harvey had brought back from Italy.

Harvey returned to his laboratory. He did not publish his early, tentative conclusions. He kept them to himself and went on examining animals. He was completely bound up in these investigations. Many people thought he was eccentric. Certainly he seems to have been an ill-tempered, impatient man who resented any demand on his time that took him away from his laborious researches.

Finally, in 1628, he was ready to let the world have his findings. He put them forth in a little volume of 72 pages, badly printed on cheap paper. It appeared first in Germany, apparently because the city of Frankfurt was having a book fair that year, and Harvey hoped his book would be seen at the fair.

It was called *Exercitatio anatomica de motu cordis et Sanguïnis in Animalibus*. It is generally called today—for it is still revered and studied by many medical students—simply *De Motu Cordis,* "On the Motion of the Heart."

This remarkable book puts forth the basic theory of the circulation of the blood clearly and logically: The heart contracts and relaxes endlessly, and in each systole, or contraction, blood is driven out of the heart into the arteries, returning via the veins during the diastole, or relaxation.

Harvey estimated the quantity of blood ejected during each systole as two fluid ounces. Allowing 72 heartbeats per minute, that meant that 8,640 fluid ounces of blood were expelled from the heart every hour—three times the weight of the average adult body.

Could that be possible? Harvey insisted that it was.

But, of course, that meant there had to be an endless circulation of the blood. It was unthinkable that such a vast quantity of blood could simply ebb away each hour, to be replaced by fresh blood. No, there had to be a constant cycle, a closed cycle of blood, leaving the heart through the arteries, returning by the veins.

By hard experimental work, Harvey showed that this was true. He enlarged on the work of his old teacher, Fabrizio, to show that the veins conducted blood only *to* the heart, never away from it. The valves of the veins would not permit a reverse flow.

Leaving the left side of the heart, blood was conducted through the arteries to every part of the body, and then made its way to the veins. The veins carried the blood to the right auricle of the heart; it passed to the right ventricle, then to the lungs, then back through the pulmonary veins to the heart, to the left auricle, the left ventricle, and out again to the arteries.

There was one gap in Harvey's understanding. Lacking the microscope, he had no knowledge of the capillaries, those tiny blood vessels that link the veins and the arteries. And so his explanation of how the blood gets from the arteries to the veins was hazy and incorrect. Other than this relatively minor point, however, he had comprehended the entire cycle.

There was no longer any reason to believe in "two kinds of blood." The red blood that spurted was arterial blood, spurting because the great pump of the heart was driving it. The dark blood was blood from the veins, dark after its trip through the body, making its slow way back to the heart.

The doctors of Harvey's day found all this hard to understand and still harder to accept. "In Harvey's lifetime, no man over forty believed his theory," it was said.

John Aubrey tells us in his *Brief Lives:* "I have heard him say that after his booke on the Circulation of the Blood came out, that he fell mightily in his practize, and that 'twas beleeved by the vulgar that he was crack-brained; and all the physitians were against his position and envyed him."

But the essential common sense of the theory finally brought a grudging acceptance of its truth. Reluctantly the older men came to admit that Galen's time-hallowed theories once again were incorrect. They abandoned their mystical, hazy ideas about blood circulation and adopted Harvey's down-to-earth, mechanically sound concept of endless circulation through arteries, veins, and heart. John Aubrey writes, "With much adoe at last, in about 20 or 30 yeares time, it was received in all the Universities in the world."

There were those who tried to deny that Harvey had stated anything new. They pointed to his predecessors, to Colombo, to Fabrizio, to Servetus. But those men had merely guessed at the idea of the circulation of the blood, and they had guessed vaguely at that. They neither grasped the entire concept, nor confirmed their speculations with experiment.

Harvey's reasoning was iron-hard and backed up with solid experimental evidence. His theory is a triumph of careful observation. Dip into *De Motu Cordis* anywhere, and you will see how keenly he perceived:

> If a live snake be laid open, the heart will be seen pulsating quietly, distinctly, for more than an hour, moving like a worm, contracting in its longitudinal dimensions (for it is of an oblong shape), and propelling its contents. It becomes of a paler color in the systole, of a deeper tint in the diastole; and almost all things else are seen by which I have already said that the truth I contend for is established, only that here everything takes place more slowly, and is more distinct.

> This point in particular may be observed more clearly than the

noon-day sun: the vena cava enters the heart at its lower part, the artery quits it at the superior part; the vein being now seized either with forceps or between the finger and thumb, and the course of the blood for some space below the heart interrupted, you will perceive the part that intervenes between the fingers and the heart almost immediately to become empty, the blood being exhausted by the action of the heart; at the same time the heart will become of a much paler color, even in its state of dilatation, than it was before; it is also smaller than at first, from wanting blood; and then it begins to beat more slowly, so that it seems at length as if it were about to die. But the impediment to the flow of blood being removed, instantly the color and the size of the heart are restored.

If, on the contrary, the artery instead of the vein be compressed or tied, you will observe the part between the obstacle and the heart, and the heart itself, to become inordinately distended, to assume a deep purple or even livid color, and at length to be so much oppressed with blood that you will believe it about to be choked; but the obstacle removed, all things immediately return to their natural state in color, size, and impulse.

This is not idle theorizing, building of castles in the air. This is hard scientific observation of the highest quality. William Harvey's work on the circulation of the blood is as notable for its *method* as for its conclusions. This is why it is considered one of the greatest books in the history of medicine.

Harvey's conclusions were vital to the future of surgery. Until he showed which way the blood flowed, surgeons dealing with blood vessels had to operate by sheer guesswork. How could a blood vessel be tied off with a ligature, if the surgeon did not know whether it carried blood to or from the heart?

All this changed. The ligature, rediscovered by Paré, could now be safely used in all kinds of operations. The deluge of blood that had always accompanied surgery was brought under control. The death rate from loss of blood dropped.

Although still a young man when *De Motu Cordis* was published, Harvey showed the effects of his years of patient toil. He had few friends, and his temper was notoriously short; he preferred to keep to himself.

But in 1632 he was made physician to King Charles I, and became a close friend of that amiable, intelligent, and tragic monarch, who was to be beheaded by his own people. As a friend of the King's, Harvey found himself on the losing side in the Civil War in England from 1642 to 1649. After Charles' execution, Harvey retired into solitude, his medical practice gone, his friends exiled.

In old age, however, this remarkable man turned to yet another great unsolved mystery—the study of life in the womb. "All things come from the egg," he announced, and he made pioneering studies that have since won him the rank of Father of Embryology.

At the age of 73, in 1651, he published the second of his two medical classics: *De Generatione Animalium,* "On the Generation of Animals." It was to embryology as his earlier book had been to the study of the circulatory system. John Aubrey tells us how he spent his nights doing the research for this book: "He did delight to be in the dark, and told me he could then best contemplate."

Nearing the end of his days, Harvey was chosen President of the College of Physicians, a high honor to crown his life. Few denied his greatness by this time. He died on the third of June, 1657, like Paré surviving to his 80th year. England's greatest doctors paid honor to him as he went to the grave.

Harvey's historic work on the circulatory system showed the way to a host of later men. In 1661 the Italian anatomist Marcello Malpighi, using the newly invented microscope, discovered the hair-fine blood vessels, called capillaries, that link the arteries and veins. This completed the structure Harvey had erected. Santorio Santorio of

Capodistria invented the first clinical thermometer. The German Jesuit, Athanasius Kircher, turned the microscope onto the blood of plague victims and was surprised to find a great many little "worms" lurking in the fluid.

Modern medicine was beginning to take shape.

6

Hunter: "Don't Think. Try It!"

H<small>E WAS</small> short and thick-set, with a peasant's stocky awkwardness about him. In an age when gentlemen wore powdered wigs, he defiantly showed his red hair to the world. He was coarse of feature and coarser of tongue. To look at him, you would think that he was a butcher or a street-sweeper, and not the greatest medical man of the time.

For John Hunter still lives, more than a hundred and seventy years since his death. The peruked and dandified doctors of his day exist only in the pages of medical histories—but John Hunter's name endures, not only immortalized by the Hunterian Museum in London and the Hunterian Laboratory at Johns Hopkins University in Baltimore, but enshrined forever in the minds of men of science.

He was rough and uncouth and eccentric. But his eccentricity was no bar to his greatness. Again and again, he hurled at the universe the defiant question: *"Why? Why?"* And he forced the universe to give up at least part of the answer.

John Hunter's greatest accomplishment—and there were many—lay in the field of pathology. If anatomy is the study of the normal, healthy human body, pathology is the study of the changes worked in the body by disease.

The works of Hippocrates and Galen contain many brilliant pathologic essays, describing in vivid detail the steady deterioration of the body as disease worked its ravages on it. One such essay is quoted in the chapter on Hippocrates.

But by the end of the seventeenth century, the time was ripe for a *modern* school of pathology. The new anatomy of Vesalius and his successors had changed the basis of medicine. The microscope and other new devices afforded greater accuracy of observation. There was no longer any excuse for relying on clinical descriptions that went back to the time of Hippocrates.

One of the first of the great modern pathologists was Thomas Sydenham (1624–1689), generally considered the finest clinical observer of his time. He is often called "The English Hippocrates." Sydenham set down classic descriptions of such diseases as scarlet fever, measles, and dysentery—as well as gout, that ailment of men overfond of wine. Sydenham had firsthand knowledge of the gout!

He taught that by recognizing the symptoms and effects of particular diseases in particular cases, a doctor could learn how to recognize the same process in other cases. This idea of moving from the particular to the general, which seems so obvious to us, was Sydenham's great contribution to medicine.

After Sydenham came a swarm of other doctors, each concentrating on the pathology of one particular disease: Wepfer on apoplexy, Glisson on rickets, and so forth. A concept that seems elementary, but actually was brand new, had been given to the world: the idea that each disease was unique, that the doctor must begin by diagnosis of the particular disease before he can move on to the treatment of the patient.

The eighteenth century was a time of great excitement in medicine, an unfolding of new knowledge at a pace never before equalled in all history. And one of the leaders was that rough-hewn, blustery Scot named John Hunter (1728–1793), an immortal of medicine.

Like another such immortal, William Harvey, Hunter was a short man. Like Harvey he was stubborn, independent-minded, a rugged individualist, and a brilliant doctor.

He was born on a farm called Long Calderwood, seven miles from Glasgow. The youngest of ten children, John Hunter seemed to be the least promising of the whole large family. Two of his older brothers seemed marked for greatness: handsome, elegant William, who was studying medicine, and James, who was to be a lawyer.

John was unruly and unstudious. He appeared destined to be of no account. He hated school, ignored his books, and, when angered, would howl for hours on end. He grew up disobedient and uneducated.

The only sign that he had any intelligence at all was his curiosity about nature. "When I was a boy," he once remarked, "I wanted to know all about the clouds and the grasses and why the leaves changed color in the autumn. I watched ants, bees, birds, tadpoles, and caddis-worms. I pestered people with questions about what nobody knew or cared anything about."

During John's stormy childhood, his brother William, who was ten years older, was prospering in London. The handsome and well-bred William, of whom one contemporary said, "His whole conduct was more strictly and steadily correct than that of any other young person I have ever known," was becoming one of London's most successful surgeons and anatomists. His practice had made him wealthy and socially prominent. Graceful and genteel, he had dropped his harsh Scots accent and now spoke with the polish of a London aristocrat.

William needed an assistant. Brother Jamie, finding the study of law not to his liking, came down to London and became a pupil of William's in medicine. But Jamie had tuberculosis, and soon he returned to Scotland and an early grave.

There was brother John, though. John was now 20, badly educated and without skills, a cloddish, clumsy, oaf of a boy. He was restless on the family farm. There was great energy churning in him, but he had no way of harnessing it. For a while John had been apprenticed to a carpenter and to everyone's surprise had displayed unusual ability for fine craftsmanship. But the carpenter went bankrupt. John was without employment.

He wrote to William, asking to be taken on as his assistant. If William refused him, he said, he would join the army.

William was dismayed. John was the family ne'er-do-well, and it was inconceivable that he would do well in the difficult practice of surgery. Besides, William was unwilling to display this oafish bumpkin in London and own him as his brother. John would be too vivid a reminder that William's aristocratic airs of breeding were only skin deep.

But brotherly love prevailed. William had to keep John out of trouble. In 1748, John journeyed to London, a two-week trip by horseback, and went to work as William's apprentice.

William was about to give a lecture on the anatomy of the arm. He was too busy to prepare the arm himself, so he told John, "Dissect it for me. Lay bare the veins and muscles."

Probably William thought that he would have to re-do John's work himself. But he was surprised to find that John had done a superb job of dissection, painstakingly cutting away skin and flesh and fat to reveal the underlying structure of the arm. The boy had an unsuspected talent for this delicate, demanding work. William gave him another arm to work on, this one having the blood vessels injected with colored wax to make them more easily visible. That was a new European technique William was experimenting with. Again, John surpassed William's expectation.

It was astonishing how zealously John took to the job. He was masterful at the tricky task of dissecting out muscles, blood vessels, and nerves. William had had small hope for him, but soon John was proving a valued and even indispensable assistant.

Voluntarily, John worked far into the night. For the first time in his life, he had found something that interested him, and that he excelled at.

At that time in England it was legal to dissect only the bodies of executed criminals and suicides. The supply of these necessarily was limited, and those cadavers that became available usually went to the universities. Private anatomical schools such as William Hunter's were hard pressed for cadavers with which to teach anatomy.

And so a thriving trade in black-market cadavers sprang up. In the sixteenth century, Vesalius had to do his own stealing from the grave-yards, but by the time of the Hunters, the trade was well organized. Illegal operators nicknamed "resurrectionists" would snatch bodies from graves soon after burial, and would peddle them to medical students at exorbitant rates. Since the supply of cadavers in any one place might fluctuate, there was a constant to-and-fro of bodies in pickle-brine, shipped from areas of great supply to places where bodies were in demand.

Everyone knew about the resurrectionists. There were popular jokes about them, and jingles, like this one from Thomas Hood's *Mary's Ghost:*

> *The body-snatchers, they have come,*
> *And made a snatch at me;*
> *It's very hard them kind of men*
> *Won't let a body be!*

It was John Hunter's job to purchase cadavers from the resurrectionists for use at William's school. William himself, as a wealthy and refined gentleman, was far too fastidious to deal with such ruffians himself. But he needed cadavers, all the same, so he sent his rough-hewn, coarse, and boisterous young brother out to strike the illegal bargains in flesh. John greatly enjoyed his contacts with the seamy side of London life.

He was learning surgery fast—soaking up knowledge through his pores, since no one was giving him formal instruction. William recognized John's gifts, and decided that he should have a real education. He sent him to Chelsea Hospital, then to St. Bartholomew's, for medical instruction.

But William was troubled by the fact that John lacked the general education of a gentleman. John knew nothing of literature, of the arts, of languages and learning. To remedy this, William enrolled him at Oxford.

John lasted only a few months. "They wanted to make an old woman of me, or that I should stuff Latin at the University," he said. "But these schemes I cracked like so many vermin as they came before me."

He returned to London still almost illiterate and exceedingly uncouth, and got quickly back into the only world he cared for—that of medicine. He became a student at St. George's Hospital, later joining the staff and remaining there more than twenty years.

He turned now to anatomy—comparative anatomy, the study of the same organs in many species of animal. In order to understand the functioning of human organs like the heart or the liver, he believed, it was necessary to study the way such organs worked in dogs, in cats, in snakes, even in lions and elephants if they could be had.

But his intensive studies were interrupted, in 1761, by an attack of pneumonia. "Get away from the dissecting table if you value your life," he was told. "You need some fresh air. You need a change of surroundings."

Hunter used William's influence and secured a post as a military surgeon. Unlike the ordinary army or navy surgeon, who was content to do a slapdash job on the wounded men who came his way, Hunter treated each case as a unique problem and learned much even as he healed his patients. "Every injury he had to treat was for him an experiment," one biographer has commented.

In 1763 Hunter returned to London and set up in private practice. He was nearly penniless, and he knew that unless he became a money-earning doctor, he could never hope to carry out the experiments he dreamed of.

His practice grew rapidly, until he was almost as much in demand among the wealthy as his celebrated older brother. As fast as he earned money, he spent it on his research.

He built a suburban house of fanciful design and filled it with bizarre statues and a huge menagerie, including leopards, jackals, a zebra, an opossum, and any other exotic beast he could acquire. He begged friends going abroad to ship him animals. One sent him portions of a whale, another shipped him buffaloes, and the Queen herself gave him three elephants. One of the elephants was dead, but that troubled Hunter not at all, since he intended to dissect all three.

He cut up every animal that came his way, preserving their bones and internal organs. Endlessly he worked, slicing his strange beasts up, filling the house with specimen jars and mounted skeletons. The place had a fierce smell. Odd things were always happening—as when one of the leopards broke out of its cage, and Hunter seized it barehanded and dragged it back to captivity without quite realizing the danger of what he was doing.

Londoners regarded him as an eccentric. And rightly, since he once drove a harnessed buffalo through the city streets, and that was not the least strange of his antics. He did not care what they thought. He went his own way, as rugged an individualist as has ever existed —and, as he traveled his journey, he learned more about the anatomy of animals than anyone before him had ever known.

He never put on the airs of society. He was always wigless, his hands stained with dye and perhaps the blood of dissected beasts, his clothes ruffled and askew. His thick Scots accent remained. His rough, rustic ways marked his behavior.

He startled many. When he met General James Murray, a veteran of the French and Indian War who had been seriously wounded twice, he bluntly told the General, "I would like very much to peep into your chest."

Another victim of Hunter's lack of subtlety was the composer, Franz Joseph Haydn. Haydn set several poems by Hunter's wife to music, and was frequently found in the Hunter home when he visited London. But the composer was terrified of the surgeon. Haydn had a polyp, or growth, in his nose. "You should let me remove it," Hunter told him. "It distorts your face and frightens the ladies."

Haydn had no intention of submitting to Hunter's scalpel. But Hunter wanted to study the growth, and schemed for some way of parting it from the composer's nose. He lured Haydn to his office on a flimsy pretense, and then two husky apprentices seized the Father of the Symphony and began to haul him toward an operating chair. The panicky Haydn managed to free himself.

"Do you wish to take your foe to the grave?" Hunter asked.

"Such is my intention," Haydn replied.

The composer lived to regret it. When he was old, the polyp grew bigger, and caused him great pain and discomfort. But he was too sickly to risk surgery then and had to endure the pain of "his foe" until his death.

Hunter excelled as a teacher, and where once the most popular private medical school in London was William's, now the students flocked to hear John. He spoke gruffly but well, and one of his followers, Henry Cline, wrote, "I found him so far superior to anything that I had conceived or heard, that there seemed no comparison between the great mind of the man . . . and all the individuals who had gone before, ancient or modern."

His classes were not always crowded. Once, at the beginning, he entered a classroom to find precisely one student waiting. Undaunted, John pulled a skeleton into the room, seated it, and grinning, began: "Gentlemen—"

He taught that surgery should never be used unless all else failed. The knife was the last resort. "Never perform an operation on another person which, under similar circumstances, you would not have performed on yourself."

Unlike some medical teachers, who handed out the same cut-and-dried lectures every year for decades, Hunter was forever changing his views as his experience grew. One bright student pointed out that his latest statement contradicted something he had taught the year before. "Vurra likely," Hunter retorted. "I hope I grow wiser every year." Another time, seeing his students busily taking notes of every word he said, he wagged a finger in discouragement and said, "Better not write down that observation, for vurra likely I shall think differently next year."

Hunter drove himself furiously, though in his later years he suffered from the heart ailment known as angina pectoris. He was up at dawn and worked in his dissecting room till nine. Then he saw patients at home till noon, made his round of visits till four, returned home for dinner and a nap, and gave lectures in the evening. At night, he compiled notes on his day's observations, and went to bed by one or two in the morning. He slept no more than four hours a night.

This was his daily routine for years. Though his practice brought him more than $25,000 a year—a great deal of money in those days —he spent it all, since his establishment grew to include 45 persons, including gardeners, animal keepers, and secretaries. Whatever was left beyond immediate expenses went to purchase new specimens for the collection.

He was not interested merely in exotic animals. Unusual human beings attracted him too. One of the most unusual was a young Irishman named Charles Byrne, who at the age of twenty-one stood eight feet two inches tall in his stockinged feet. Byrne came to London in 1782 with a freak show, and among the thousands who paid two shillings sixpence to view him was John Hunter. Hunter felt an immediate itch to own the giant's body and, by dissecting it, to find out what had caused it to attain such great size.

"Giants are usually short-lived," Hunter bluntly told the unhappy Irishman. "Your body has scientific value, so when you die, it should be left to me for dissection."

All this talk of early death and dissection terrified the slow-witted young giant, and he fled from Hunter. The surgeon followed him grimly, hiring a detective to trail him and report on the state of Byrne's health. Soon Byrne fell ill. Unwilling to yield his body up to the dissecting knife, the giant made his friends promise that after his death, his body would be sunk in a lead-lined coffin in the middle of the Irish channel.

Hearing this, a group of London medical students constructed a diving bell, so that they could recover the body from the waters and present it to Hunter. But the diving operation was not necessary. Byrne died shortly, at 22. Hunter himself waylaid the giant's friends, got them drunk, and bribed them heavily to turn the body over to him.

During the night Hunter smuggled the huge corpse to his museum. He cut it up, boiled the flesh from the bones, and mounted the skeleton. It is still to be seen at the Hunterian Museum of the Royal College of Surgeons in London—a prize exhibit that was luckily spared when a German bomb destroyed two-thirds of Hunter's collection in 1941. It is perhaps the most famous skeleton in the world. In 1909 the brain surgeon Harvey Cushing was permitted to saw off the top of the skull to examine it, and he found evidences of a brain tumor that had caused the unusual height.

Hunter was in constant correspondence with many of the leading medical men of the day, most notably Edward Jenner, the discoverer of the smallpox vaccine, whom we will meet in the next chapter. Much of this correspondence survives. In one letter to Hunter, Jenner writes, "Have you made any experiments with hedgehogs, and can you send me some this spring? for all those you sent me died and I am hedgehogless." Another, more perplexing statement to Jenner was, "Frogs live an amazing time after they are dead."

All this ceaseless activity, this collecting and dissecting would have been mere eccentricity had it not been combined with a searching mind. Hunter was spectacularly able to draw conclusions from the wealth of evidence he surveyed. He became one of the outstanding scientific minds of his time, far exceeding his more respectable but less brilliant brother William, who died in 1783. There was the touch of madness about John Hunter, but also the undoubted touch of greatness.

One of his biographers, Stephen Paget, says of him that he was "anatomist, biologist, naturalist, physician, surgeon and pathologist, all at once and all in the highest. . . . Contrast him with Ambroise Paré, a surgeon in some ways like him, shrewd, observant, ahead of his age; the achievements of Paré, side by side with those of Hunter, are like child's play in comparison with the serious affairs of men; Paré advanced the art of surgery, but Hunter taught the science of it."

And what were these accomplishments of Hunter, aside from the hounding of sick giants and the carving up of dead elephants?

He did not leave behind a vast collection of writings, as did Galen or Paré. He wrote only two books. The first, *On Venereal Diseases*, served as the basic work on that troublesome subject for almost a century. The book was a testament to the experimental art—to the reliance on observation, rather than theory and deductions, which has always been at the core of true medical advancement.

Even more important was his second book, *A Treatise on the Blood, Inflammation, and Gunshot Wounds*, published in 1794, a year after his death. This is a landmark in the science of pathology. Hunter's valuable contribution was a recognition that inflammation was not a disease in itself, as was thought, but a stage in the development of diseases in general. He understood that inflammation could be of several types, had several causes, and was not necessarily harmful to the body. He wrote:

> Inflammation in itself is not to be considered as a disease, but as a salutary operation, consequent either to some violence or some disease. . . . Inflammation is not only occasionally the cause of diseases, but it is often a mode of cure. . . .

Aside from these books, he left huge quantities of notes and observations. Much of this was never published, but was burned after Hunter's death by his brother-in-law, Everard Home, who had drawn liberally on them for his own writings and wanted to conceal the evidence of his thefts.

Hunter's zealous work also brought surgery back to the main stream of medicine. In his day, surgeons and doctors were considered members of separate professions. Surgery was thought to be lower, and when a surgeon wished to become a doctor of medicine, he had first to renounce the practice of surgery. William Hunter was one of the many who did this. The surgeon was considered a mere technician, a sculptor in flesh. In part this way of thinking was a remnant of the medieval days when surgery was practiced by barbers.

Hunter, though, was clearly much more than a mere technician, a knife-wielder. He was a man of science. He spanned the world of medicine as well as the more limited world of surgery, and by his example the surgeon rejoined the fellowship of doctors. Though no gentleman himself, he helped make surgery a gentleman's profession.

He died in debt. His heart condition had kept him on the brink of death for years—"My life," he said, "is at the mercy of the first rascal who chooses to annoy me"—and he died of a heart attack in 1793, during a particularly argumentative wrangle over hospital procedures. His great collection was eventually bought by the British Government for some $75,000—about a fifth of what he had spent on it.

Hunter's scientific accomplishments were vast, so that one nineteenth-century historian was able to say, "When we make a discovery in pathology we only learn what we have overlooked in his writings or forgotten in his lectures." His influence as a teacher was as great as his own work. His most brilliant pupil was Edward Jenner, who once came to him to say that he thought he could prevent smallpox by vaccination.

"Don't think," Hunter retorted. "Try it! Be patient, be accurate!" And Jenner spent the next eighteen years in painstaking observation.

Dr. Henry Sigerist offers an able summary of the place of John Hunter in medical history:

> It seems to me, then, that Hunter's main significance was that he threw open the field of surgical observation and experiment to general medicine, enabling all doctors to turn it to account. He was a working surgeon like the rest of them; but he was also a man of science. For him a wound was something more than a practical problem. He was not content to ask, "How can I best heal this wound?" He inquired, "What does the wound signify to the organism? By what mechanisms does the organism safeguard itself against the effects of the wound, immediate and remote?"
> In this way, almost imperceptibly, he passed from the domain

of surgery into that of pathology. His anatomical and physio-logical studies safeguarded him against getting lost in a maze of speculation. As a practitioner, he advanced by practical meas-ures, set the organism tasks, made experiments. Not having been trained as a physician, approaching the problems devoid of pre-conceptions and from without, he saw much which had remained hidden from the doctors.

Along this path he was a pioneer hastening greatly in advance of his time, and he constructed the first bridge between surgery and medicine.

7

Jenner: "I Selected a Healthy Boy..."

In 1770 there came to London a young doctor from Gloucestershire, a clergyman's son named Edward Jenner, to study with the great John Hunter. Jenner was twenty-one, cheerful, round-faced and smiling, with short, curly hair and a stocky build not unlike Hunter's. He had studied surgery and pharmacology in the provinces, and now he had come to London to add to his store of medical knowledge. His main ambition was to return to his home and be a successful country doctor. He did not hunger for fame or wealth—but fame found him anyway, and wealth could have been his had he wanted it.

Like Hunter, Jenner had spent his boyhood studying nature. He had collected birds' eggs and fossils, had filled notebooks with his findings, had satisfied his curiosity in every field of science. Once, when his friends were arguing whether a candle flame was hotter at its center or its tip, Jenner settled the problem with youthful directness. He lit a candle, poked his finger into the flame, and held it there for a moment or two. Then he tried to hold his hand at the tip of the flame, but had to pull back at once. "There, gentlemen," he announced. "The question is settled!"

He grew up a pleasant, capable young man, not at all like the rough, crusty Hunter. Jenner could sing, played several musical instruments, wrote music and poetry. But his chief interest was medicine. In his teens, he became a surgeon's apprentice. When he was 19, a young farm girl came to him for medical advice, and Jenner asked her, routinely, if she had ever had smallpox.

"No," she said. "I cannot take that disease, for I have had the cowpox."

Another man might have brushed the girl's statement aside as just another bit of country misinformation. But Jenner remembered it. The idea remained with him—and led him, eventually, to make an epochal medical discovery.

Smallpox was an ancient and dreaded disease in Jenner's day. It killed nearly half of its victims, and left the rest blind, crippled, horridly disfigured. "The most terrible of all the ministers of death," the historian Macaulay called it. One death out of every ten was caused by smallpox. Few reached adulthood without showing signs of the disease's ravages. George Washington's face was pitted by the craterlike pockmarks of smallpox. Queen Maria Theresa of Austria lost her beauty to it. Louis XV of France died of it.

In a single year in Russia, two million died of the pox. Since the beginning of the eighteenth century, forty million had perished of it throughout the world. An average year saw 200,000 dying of it in Europe, where medical practice was on a high level, and the toll it took in more backward parts of the world was frightful and uncountable.

There was only one bright aspect of smallpox. Those who had it once never fell victim again. If you could only survive it, you needed not fear it thereafter.

In the Orient, this observation was put to a practical use. Healthy people were inoculated with smallpox deliberately. The attack was usually a mild one, and left the inoculated person protected for the rest of his life. There were terrible risks, of course. It was not always true that the attack would be a mild one. Disfigurement or death often resulted from inoculation.

A globe-trotting noblewoman, Lady Mary Wortley Montagu,

brought inoculation to England with her from Turkey. In 1717, living
in Constantinople, she first heard of the practice. She herself had had
her beauty marred by smallpox, and her nephew and only brother
had died of it. She wrote to a friend:

> I am going to tell you a thing that I am sure will make you wish
> yourself here. The smallpox, so fatal, and so general amongst us,
> is here entirely harmless by the invention of ingrafting, which is
> the term they give it. There is a set of old women who make it
> their business to perform the operation every autumn, in the
> month of September, when the great heat is abated. People send
> to one another to know if any of their family has a mind to have
> the smallpox; they make parties for this purpose, and when they
> are met (commonly fifteen or sixteen together), the old woman
> comes with a nut-shell full of the matter of the best sort of small-
> pox, and asks what veins you please to have opened.
>
> She immediately rips open that you offer to her with a large
> needle (which gives you no more pain than a common scratch)
> and puts into the vein as much venom as can lie upon the head
> of a needle, and after binds up the little wound with a hollow bit
> of shell; and in this manner opens four or five veins. The Grecians
> have commonly the superstition of opening one in the middle
> of the forehead, in each arm and on the breast, to mark the sign of
> the cross; but this has a very ill effect, all these wounds leaving
> little scars, and is not done by those that are not superstitious,
> who choose to have them in the legs, or that part of the arm that
> is concealed.
>
> The children or young patients play together all the rest of the
> day, and are in perfect health to the eighth. Then the fever be-
> gins to seize them, and they keep to their beds two days, very
> seldom three. Every year thousands undergo this operation; and
> the French ambassador says pleasantly, that they take the small-
> pox here by way of diversion, as they take the waters in other
> countries. There is no example of any one that has died of it;

and you may believe I am very well satisfied of the safety of this experiment, since I intend to try it on my dear little son.

Lady Montagu's son came through inoculation successfully, and later so did her daughter. When she returned to England, she attempted to get the British doctors to adopt the practice, but most of them refused. Lady Montagu angrily accused them of wanting to maintain the spread of smallpox for the sake of their own pocketbooks.

Gradually the practice took hold. One man, Dr. Thomas Dimsdale of London, was so successful at inoculating that he was invited to inoculate Frederick the Great of Prussia, the Crown Prince of Denmark, and then Catherine the Great of Russia, who gave him a barony and a fortune for his troubles.

But inoculation had its drawbacks. Its mortality rate was low— only about three percent of those inoculated died of it—but it tended to spread smallpox to the uninoculated. Smallpox is one of the most contagious diseases known. Inoculation caused a mild attack of smallpox, but the inoculated persons passed the disease along in a deadly form to those who were not protected.

One of those who was inoculated was Edward Jenner, aged eight. The annals of his native town, Berkeley, record the fact: "He was a fine ruddy boy and, at eight years of age, was, with many others, put under a preparatory process for inoculation with the smallpox. This preparation lasted for six weeks. He was bled to ascertain whether his blood was fine; was purged repeatedly, till he became emaciated and feeble; was kept on a very low diet . . . and dosed with a diet-drink to sweeten the blood. After this barbarism of human veterinary practice, he was removed to one of the usual inoculation stables, and haltered up with others, in a terrible state of disease."

Jenner spent two years studying with John Hunter. Then he returned to Berkeley, an ancient market town in a particularly beautiful part of England. Jenner rarely left Berkeley again, and as Hunter rarely quitted London, they saw little of each other in later years. But they corresponded regularly. Jenner carefully kept every one of the great man's letters.

Hunter bothered Jenner endlessly for animal specimens. Hunter needed "a large porpoise, for love or money." He begged for black-birds, for crows, and, as we have seen, for hedgehogs. Jenner sent him a cuckoo's stomach, and Hunter wrote, "I should like to have a few more, for they do not all show the same thing. If possible, I wish you could remove the cuckoo's egg into another bird's nest, and tame the young, to see what note it has. There is employment for you, young man!"

The correspondence is full of such requests. Jenner was asked to take the temperature of bats; to examine eels in hopes of finding the difference between their sexes; to bore holes in trees to see whether the sap flowed in winter. In return, Hunter combed the art galleries of London for paintings to send to the picture-loving Jenner.

For Jenner, the years passed quietly in rural Berkeley. He loved the life of a country doctor, shunning the ugly cities and avoiding any medical controversies. The only dark moment of his life came when he was jilted: He was about to marry a wealthy young lady, but she changed her mind. Unhappily, Jenner sent the news to Hunter, who was not greatly sympathetic.

"I can easily conceive how you must feel," Hunter wrote him, "for you have two passions to cope with, viz., that of being disappointed in love, and that of being defeated; but both will wear out, perhaps the first soonest . . . 'let her go, never mind her.' I shall employ you with hedgehogs."

Another topic employed Jenner's attention during these quiet years: the relationship between smallpox and cowpox.

Cowpox, or *vaccinia,* is a minor disease of cattle. As in smallpox in humans, *pustules,* or blisterlike pimples, appeared on the udders of infected cows. The disease could be transmitted to humans. Milkmaids and farmers who handled infected cows might, if they had a scratch or a cut on their fingers, develop cowpox themselves. Neither in cows nor in humans was the disease a very serious one. It caused a slight fever, nothing more. In a few days the pustules dried, forming scabs, that dropped off, leaving faint scars.

Jenner's Gloucestershire was dairy country, and he had plenty of opportunity to observe cowpox. There was the old country legend that those who had had cowpox were immune to smallpox, and this seemed to be true. Queens might have pitted and scarred faces, but most milkmaids had near-perfect complexions.

Jenner wondered if, perhaps, there might be some way of protecting people against smallpox by giving them cowpox deliberately. It might be far more effective than the risky process of inoculation then in use.

He mentioned the matter to Hunter, telling the older man how he thought cowpox might give protection. It brought forth Hunter's famous reply: "Don't think. Try it!"

But Jenner was not a hasty man. He continued to study the two diseases in and around Berkeley. The more he saw, the more convinced he was that he was right. There were cases where milkmaids were inoculated with smallpox and failed to develop the usual fever and blisters. It turned out that they had all previously had cowpox—some of them many decades before. It appeared that cowpox did, indeed, give lasting protection against the more dangerous disease. But Jenner proceeded slowly. From 1773 on, he kept records of his observations.

In 1788, when he was thirty-nine, he fell in love again, and married. A year later he became a father. He wrote to Hunter, asking him to be the child's godfather. Hunter replied, "I wish you joy. . . . Rather than the brat should not be a Christian I will stand godfather, for I should be unhappy if the poor little thing should go to the devil. . . . I hope Mrs. Jenner is well, and that you begin to look grave now that you are a father."

The years passed. Jenner piled up notebook after notebook on cowpox. In 1789 he wrote to a friend, Edward Gardener, that he believed he had discovered a way to end the threat of smallpox. "I have entrusted a most important matter to you," he wrote, "which I firmly believe will prove of essential benefit to the human race. I know you, and should not wish what I have stated brought into conversation; for, should anything untoward turn up in my experiments, I should be made, particularly by my medical brethren, the subject of ridicule. . . ."

Seven more years of painstaking, careful observations passed before Jenner felt bold enough to put his thoughts into action. During those years he had tried many minor experiments. He had inoculated several milkmaids with smallpox matter after they had had cowpox. None of them contracted smallpox. But there were problems. Sometimes a girl who had had cowpox *did* later come down with smallpox. Jenner later discovered why: there were several types of diseases that farmers called cowpox, but only one type provided protection against smallpox. Also, the cowpox disease was sometimes too weak to give immunity. The immunity did not "take."

In 1796, Jenner made his most celebrated experiment. A dairymaid named Sarah Nelmes came down with cowpox. She had scratched her finger on a thorn, and then had milked infected cows. Her hands developed the pustules of cowpox.

Jenner extracted some of the matter from Sarah Nelmes' pustules. Then, as he tells us, "I selected a healthy boy, about eight years old, for the purpose of inoculation for the cowpox." On May 14, 1796, Jenner made two half-inch incisions in the arms of a farmer's brave son, James Phipps, and inserted the cowpox matter.

James developed the pustules of cowpox. He had a fever and a headache, but they subsided. The pustules withered, and the scabs dropped off, leaving little scars. Within two weeks the boy was back in perfect health.

On July 1, Jenner took the next step. He inoculated the boy with fluid taken from a smallpox pustule. And he waited. Would young Phipps develop smallpox?

He did not. He did not even show the minor signs of irritation, the mild form of the disease that inoculation customarily produced. Jenner wrote to Gardener, "The boy has since been inoculated for the smallpox which, as I ventured to predict, produced no effect. I shall now pursue my experiments with redoubled ardor."

Jenner had carried out the first *vaccination*.

There is an interesting problem in the meaning of words here. Remember that another name for cowpox was *vaccinia*. The name came from the Latin word *vacca,* meaning "cow." The original meaning of the word *vaccine* was "fluid taken from a cowpox pustule." And *vaccination* was the act of injecting vaccine into a human being.

Vaccination was originally put forth as a different process from *inoculation,* which mean the deliberate injection of smallpox matter into the body in the hope of bringing about immunity. But as time passed all the terms lost their original meanings. Today "vaccination" and "inoculation" are used interchangeably. And the link between *vacca* and *vaccine* has been forgotten. Nowadays there are vaccinations against many diseases—polio, diphtheria, tetanus, etc.—which have nothing to do with cows or cowpox.

After his experiments with James Phipps, Jenner was satisfied that he had demonstrated the connection between cowpox and smallpox. He had taken the old wives' tale about cowpox giving immunity to smallpox, and, as he said, he had "placed it on a rock where I knew it would be immovable before I invited the public to take a look at it."

Jenner made his work public later in 1796. He notified the Royal Society, England's great scientific body, but the Society rejected his paper. They would not hear the unknown country doctor. Possibly, if John Hunter were alive, Jenner might have been able to get a hearing. But Hunter was three years in his grave.

"Perhaps if you wrote a book, you would be heard," a friend suggested. Jenner agreed. He returned to Berkeley, restudied his evidence, and compiled a manuscript. In 1798 he traveled to London to give his manuscript to a publisher. He took with him some vaccine, which he left with a surgeon named Henry Cline, another of Hunter's old pupils. Cline was the only doctor who would listen to Jenner in the three months he spent in London.

Jenner left for Berkeley again. Cline, meanwhile, experimented with the vaccine on a child with tuberculosis of the hip. Cline's main idea was to create an inflammation that would relieve the pain in the diseased joint, after the manner of a mustard plaster. But Cline could not resist also inoculating for smallpox. In August, 1798, he wrote to Jenner:

> The cowpox experiment has succeeded admirably. The child sickened on the seventh day; and the fever, which was moderate, subsided on the eleventh day. The inflammation extended to about four inches diameter, and then gradually subsided. . . . I have inoculated him with smallpox matter in three places, which were slightly inflamed on the third day, and then subsided. Dr. Lister, who was formerly physician to the Smallpox Hospital, attended the child with me, and he is convinced that it is not possible to give him the smallpox.
>
> I think the substituting of cowpox poison for the smallpox promises to be one of the greatest improvements that has ever been made in medicine; for it is not only so safe in itself, but also does not endanger others by contagion. . . .

Jenner's book appeared that same year. Like so many of the classics of medicine, it is little more than a pamphlet, only 75 pages long. It bore the imposing title, *An Inquiry into the Causes and Effects of the Variolae Vaccine, a Disease Discovered in some of the western counties of England, particularly Gloucestershire, and known by the name of the Cowpox.*

The book was an immediate sensation. Though hardly anyone actually read it, everyone was talking about it. Cowpox and vaccination became topics of universal discussion. Many doctors embraced the new technique enthusiastically. Others were violently opposed, since every new advance in medicine must win its way by defeating the objections of the conservatives.

Cartoonists attacked Jenner, showing vaccinated people sprouting cowhorns and talking in moos. Pamphlets were written attacking him. Not everyone was as careful in vaccinating as Jenner. Quacks often used contaminated vaccine under unsanitary conditions. Sometimes the puncture was too deep, which caused serious illness. Or the wrong type of cowpox was used, providing no immunity. Every failure of vaccination was seized upon as proof of the worthlessness of the entire method.

Throughout the storm, Jenner remained at his country home, quietly continuing his researches. Henry Cline wrote to him, asking him to come to London to enter practice there. Cline assured him that he would earn £10,000—$50,000 then—a year in London. But Jenner had no desire to leave Berkeley. He sent Cline this remarkable answer:

> Shall I, who even in the morning of my days sought the lowly and sequestered paths of life, the valley and not the mountains; shall I, now that my evening is fast approaching, hold myself up as an object for fortune and fame? Admitting it as a certainty that I obtain both, what stock should I add to my little fund of happiness? My fortune, with what flows in from my profession, is sufficient to gratify my wishes; indeed, so limited is my ambition, and that of my dearest connexions, that were I precluded from further practice, I should be enabled to obtain all I want. As for fame, what is it? A gilded butt, forever pierced with the arrows of malignancy. . . .

He was not allowed to have the peace he craved. He knew more about vaccination than any other man, and with each new smallpox epidemic, he was asked to teach others his methods. In his own words, he became "the vaccine clerk of the world." But the idea of vaccination spread, and the results were amazing. In America, President Jefferson had his family and friends vaccinated. In Cuba, where smallpox had been the grimmest of killers, two years went by without a smallpox fatality. In France, two and a half million people were vaccinated, and only seven developed smallpox.

A Royal Jennerian Society was founded. The name of Jenner was known around the world. When England went to war with France, Jenner begged Napoleon to release some English prisoners. "Ah," said Napoleon, "we can refuse nothing to that man." The prisoners went free.

In Canada, the chiefs of the Five Indian Nations composed this letter that was sent to Jenner:

> Brother! Our Father has delivered to us the book you sent to instruct us how to use the discovery which the Great Spirit made to you, whereby the smallpox, that fatal enemy of our tribes, may be driven from the earth. We have deposited your book in the hands of the man of skill whom our great Father employs to attend us when sick or wounded.
>
> We shall not fail to teach our children to speak the name of Jenner; and to thank the Great Spirit for bestowing upon him so much wisdom and so much benevolence.
>
> We send with this a belt and a string of Wampum, in token of your precious gift; and we beseech the Great Spirit to take care of you in this world and in the land of spirits.

Despite these honors, Jenner often wearied of his fame. In 1802, he was persuaded by friends to apply to Parliament for a monetary grant. He had spent most of his own funds during his long years of research, and now his time was so much in demand that he was not free to earn his living as a doctor. He petitioned Parliament, but unwillingly, and many of vaccination's opponents spoke out against giving him public funds. "I sometimes wish this business had never been brought forward," Jenner finally declared. "It makes me feel indignant to reflect that one who has, through a most painful and laborious investigation, brought to light a subject that will add to the happiness of every human being in the world, should appear among his countrymen as a supplicant for the means of obtaining a few comforts for himself and family."

Parliament voted him £10,000. But he continued to spend his

funds to promote the development and improvement of vaccination. To a friend who thought he had grown wealthy from his discovery, Jenner wrote:

> I know you fancy that the *cow* has fattened me, and that it is of no use to attempt altering your opinion. My domestication is the same now as it was before I cultivated her acquaintance so closely; except, that *then I had horses to my carriage,* and that *now I have none.* . . .

Jenner's son died in 1810, his wife in 1815. His old age was a lonely one, but made brighter by the knowledge of the boon he had given mankind. On a bitterly cold January day in 1823, when Jenner was in his 74th year, he walked to a nearby village to arrange for distribution of fuel to the poor. Coming home, he took to his bed, and the next morning suffered a paralytic stroke. He died a day later.

Jenner changed the world as few men have been privileged to do. Today, smallpox is virtually an unknown disease wherever the concept of vaccination has reached. Hundreds of millions of people have been able to reach adulthood unmarred by that sinister disease. As Thomas Jefferson said in a letter to Jenner:

> You have erased from the calendar of human afflictions one of its greatest. Yours is the comfortable reflection that mankind can never forget that you have lived; future nations will know by history only that the loathesome smallpox has existed, and by you has been extirpated.

8

McDowell: A Leap in the Dark

SURGERY at the outset of the nineteenth century had come a long way from the days of the cautery and of spouting blood, and of Ambroise Paré's puppydog medicines. The anatomy of the body was well understood. The circulation of the blood was no longer a mystery. Hospital superintendents were beginning to eliminate dirt and overcrowding. The diagnosis of disease had improved a thousand-fold. Many medical superstitions were on their way out.

In the seventeenth century, eight out of ten patients who underwent surgery died, and the survivors were usually dreadfully maimed. By the nineteenth, the average patient had at least a fighting chance to survive. Shock and bleeding and pain still carried off multitudes. But "surgeon" no longer was synonymous with "butcher."

At the outset of the new century, a spirit of vigor and boldness swept through all of medicine. Great strides were in the making. In the century to come, medicine would leap forward further in a mere ten decades than it had in all the thousands of years between Imhotep and John Hunter.

The pioneers of that century were men standing at the brink of the abyss that is the unknown. Some of them moved inch by inch down the walls of that abyss, mapping and charting as they went. Others preferred to make a headlong leap into the dark chasm.

One of the headlong leapers was an American doctor named Ephraim McDowell, who practiced in the rough pioneer country of the southeast. He was born in 1771, and when he was twenty-two he went to Europe, to the great medical school at the University of Edinburgh.

He must have cut an odd figure there, this Kentucky backwoodsman. Tall and burly and broad-shouldered, with the easy smile and simple ways of a frontiersman, he was altogether a different breed from the city-bred European boys who were his classmates. The United States was only a few years old. Perhaps he was the first American many of the boys had seen. He was a real curiosity to them.

It had been a bold thing for the McDowell family to do, sending their boy all the way to Scotland to learn doctoring. In that innocent era, many men in the United States set up as doctors or surgeons without any formal training whatever. They enjoyed a kind of on-the-job education, at the expense of their patients' lives. Those who wanted a formal medical education usually studied at Philadelphia. Why go to Europe? Especially if your only ambition was to be a country doctor?

That was the way the McDowells did things, it seems. Ephraim's father, a judge, wanted his son to have the best of training—which meant Edinburgh. What did it matter that it was a bold and costly thing to do? McDowells had always been bold—and Ephraim was to prove the boldest of them all!

He had a hard time of it at Edinburgh. He had no more than a gradeschool education when he entered medical school, and he had trouble fighting his way through the medical textbooks. On the other hand, he had already had some practical experience in medicine, as an apprentice in Virginia. He studied hard, but was no outstanding student.

He learned surgical technique at Edinburgh—the treatment of wounds, the removal of exterior tumors, and the like. The late John Hunter had developed some remarkable methods of blood-vessel surgery, and McDowell learned a little about that. And he was taught that the abdominal cavity was strictly off bounds for a surgeon. No one survived abdominal operations.

He didn't get his medical degree. Apparently his money ran out. In 1795, after two years at Edinburgh, he returned to Kentucky, setting up practice at Danville.

The fact that he had had only two years of medical school troubled his patients not at all. That was two years more than most of the Kentucky doctors had had! And McDowell had studied at a foreign university, which was all the more impressive. He soon was well known and well liked in Kentucky.

McDowell practiced in a rough and ready section. The settlers lived in sparsely situated log cabins, and the doctor riding from one settlement to the next was menaced by panthers and by occasional hostile Indians. There was no need for nicety in such a raw environment. A doctor had to be a man of firm conviction, able to face any sort of challenge, medical or otherwise.

By 1809, he had been practicing fourteen years. On a snowy, blustery December night, a stranger rapped sharply on the front door of Dr. McDowell's Danville house. The doctor peered out into the night.

"Can you come right away, doctor?" a man asked him. "Thomas Crawford's wife Jane is very sick. They say she may die. It's a long way, but they asked for you."

"What's the trouble?"

The man shrugged. "She's pregnant and she's gone into labor. But the baby won't come. She's having these terrible pains. Two doctors looked at her already, but they don't know what's wrong."

McDowell ordered his horse to be saddled, and off he went, sixty miles through the snowy night to the frontier settlement where the Crawfords had their farm. The journey took him two days. At last he arrived at the clearing in the woods where Thomas Crawford waited worriedly for him.

Jane Todd Crawford was 47 years old—late in life to be pregnant. She had already had five children successfully, but this sixth pregnancy was presenting problems. There she lay, weak with pain, her abdomen swollen.

"I'm with child," she said faintly. "But it's been ten months, doctor. And the pains—they won't stop—"

Dr. McDowell frowned. A ten-month pregnancy? That was so unusual as to seem almost impossible. He examined her, and, thanks to his Edinburgh education, was able to see what the two local doctors that had examined Jane Crawford had not realized.

"You aren't pregnant at all," he declared bluntly. "You've got a tumor. An ovarian tumor."

An ovarian tumor, or ovarian cyst, is a mass of fibrous tissue and liquid that can develop in a woman's ovary. Such cysts are relatively common, and today they are fairly easily removed before they reach any considerable size. In McDowell's time, though, it was thought impossible to remove such a cyst. They would grow and grow and grow until they filled the whole abdomen, and death would soon follow, though not before agonizing pain had been experienced.

McDowell stated the situation clearly and frankly. "If I do nothing, you will soon die in great pain, and no doubt of it. If I operate to remove this cyst, you may also die in great pain, but at least there is a chance. One way there is hope, the other there is none. Which shall it be?"

Jane Crawford chose to risk the operation.

You must understand that in 1809 doctors felt it would inevitably be fatal to open the peritoneum, which is the membrane lining the body cavity. The only internal surgical operations that were ever performed were cuttings for kidney and bladder stones. These operations, though risky enough, at least did not require cutting through the peritoneum. Otherwise, the surgeon's realm was external—amputations and the removal of external tumors. Entering the peritoneum, or that other important membrane, the pleura or lining of the chest, was simply not done.

A great eighteenth-century surgeon, Cheselden, had performed one

operation in which a woman had survived the opening of the peritoneum. But he regarded it as absolutely unique, a blind stroke of luck
that could never be repeated. Such operations as Caesarian deliveries,
in which a baby is taken from its mother through an incision in the
abdomen, almost always resulted in the death of the mother.

John Hunter, in his bold way, had written, "I cannot see any
reason why, when the disease can be ascertained in an early stage, we
should not make an opening into the abdomen and extract the cyst
itself." But he had never actually performed such an operation.

No one had.

Ephraim McDowell was about to leap headlong into the unknown.

He asked Mrs. Crawford to come to Danville, for he did not want
to risk performing the operation in her log cabin. "I'll need my
assistants," he told her. "And my instruments. You'll be more com-
fortable at my place."

She made the journey on horseback, with the huge tumor propped
on the horn of her sidesaddle. It was a slow trip. It took her four days
to cover the sixty miles.

McDowell gave her time to rest from this grueling journey. He
chose Christmas Day, 1809, for the operation. A deeply religious
man, McDowell tried always to perform risky operations on Sundays
or holy days, for he felt that on such days God would be closer to him
as he wielded the knife, and that the prayers of the congregation in
church would aid him. Before each operation he would write out a
prayer and place it in his pocket.

He wrote out a lengthy prayer this time. "Direct me, Oh! God," he
begged, "in performing this operation for I am but an instrument in
Thy hands. . . . Oh! spare this afflicted woman."

McDowell prepared for the "experiment." An experiment it was,
as Jane Crawford well knew. She had only a slim chance of surviving
the operation.

The people of Danville had learned of the experiment too, and they took the news badly. "It's nothing but sheer murder," they exclaimed. "He's deliberately going to kill that poor woman!"

There was talk of lynching McDowell if the operation failed. An angry mob supposedly gathered in front of McDowell's home as he prepared to operate. All the good will he had built over the years, as Danville's leading doctor, evaporated overnight. McDowell realized that, even if he escaped lynching as tempers cooled, a failure in this impossible operation might mean the end of his medical practice in Kentucky. He might be driven from town by outraged folk angered at his presumption in taking a sick woman's life on Christmas Day.

McDowell ignored the uproar and went ahead with the operation. He was aided by his nephew, James McDowell, and another doctor, Alban Smith. They laid Mrs. Crawford out on a wooden table, and removed the garments that covered the tumor itself, allowing her to remain in her dress. With a pen, McDowell traced the line where the incision would be made. Mrs. Crawford began to recite psalms.

There was no anesthetic to dull the pain. No antiseptic solutions were applied to prevent infection. Anesthesia and antisepsis still lay decades in the future.

McDowell selected a scalpel and handed it to his nephew, who made the first cut along the line McDowell had drawn. McDowell continued the incision himself, until a nine-inch-long cut had been made. Jane Crawford remained conscious. She went on chanting psalms. Women were made of stern stuff in Kentucky in those days.

The people of Danville were at church while the operation proceeded. On the pulpit, the preacher was denouncing men who "dared to take God's decisions into their own hands." There was no need to mention the name of Ephraim McDowell. Everyone knew who was meant.

In the doctor's home, the operation went on. It was impossible to lift the tumor out in one piece. McDowell moved it to one side, studying it, and then tied a ligature around its stem to control bleeding. Then began the job of slicing the tumor out. McDowell wrote later,

"We then cut into the tumor and took out fifteen pounds of a dirty, gelatinous-looking substance. After that we extracted the sack, which weighed seven and one half pounds."

Finally, the tumor removed, McDowell turned Mrs. Crawford to one side to drain away the accumulated blood, and stitched up the incision. The operation had last twenty-five minutes.

"She's alive!" went the word to the people of Danville. "The operation's over! She lived!"

But now came a time of waiting and fearing, for Ephraim McDowell. True enough, the tumor was out. But would the patient survive? Or would she fall victim to peritonitis—infection of the peritoneum—as was supposed to happen invariably when the abdominal wall was breached?

A day passed, two days, three, and no infection developed. On the fifth day, McDowell entered Jane Crawford's room to find her up and busily making her bed.

"I'm not used to lying around," she said.

Sternly, McDowell ordered her back to rest, and managed to keep her off her feet for the rest of the month. But he must have felt a certain inner pleasure at seeing how lively she was. Within a month, Jane was back with her family, and she lived 32 years after the operation, dying at 79.

It was an astonishing feat, both for patient and for surgeon. McDowell's boldness was matched by Mrs. Crawford's braveness. At the dedication of the McDowell Memorial in Danville many years later, Dr. Lewis A. Sayre declared that "the success of the operation and the success of the establishment of abdominal surgery were due as much to the courage of the patient as to the daring of the surgeon."

Perhaps a woman of weaker stuff would have died of shock. Perhaps. But Jane Crawford survived.

It was seven years before McDowell published the results of his astounding operation, and by that time he had successfully operated for ovarian cysts twice more. (He had also cut for gallstones many times. One of his patients was a 17-year-old boy named James Knox Polk who would one day be President.)

Finally McDowell wrote his report. It was short and simple, the work of a busy man. The *Eclectic Reportory* of Philadelphia published it in 1817.

The medical profession reacted to the unprecedented news of these operations with a mixture of disdain and anger. Many important medical authorities simply ignored the report, as if trying to pretend the whole thing had never happened. Others openly sniped at McDowell, all but calling him a liar. One of these was the editor of the London *Medico-Chirugical Review,* who said, "In spite of all that has been written in respect to this cruel operation, we entirely disbelieve that it has ever been performed with success, nor do we think it ever will."

McDowell withstood all this criticism well enough. He fought back in writing, and delivered himself of some angry remarks about specialist surgeons, mere knife-wielders, as opposed to general practitioners.

In 1825, he belatedly got his M.D. degree, from the University of Maryland. But little other fame came to him in his own time. His celebrated operation was deemed too risky, and no other doctor dared to perform it. McDowell himself cut for ovarian cysts (the operation is known as an *ovariotomy*) thirteen times in all. Eight patients lived. Four died of the operation. One operation ended in failure when other circumstances prevented removal of the tumor.

The only explanation of McDowell's phenomenal success with this "impossible" operation is that luck, or perhaps divine providence, rode with him. How he kept his patients free of infection is unknown. He must have been unusually clean in his working habits to have had such good luck in surgery, in that era before antisepsis.

On a spring day in 1830, Ephraim McDowell went into his garden to pick strawberries, and ate a great many of them off the vine. He felt sick soon after, and took to his bed. A fellow physician diagnosed his trouble as "inflammation of the stomach," which is not a very informative label. McDowell believed he had swallowed some kind of poisonous insect with the strawberries. The inflammation grew worse and there was no way to save him. He died of an abdominal ailment which could not be operated on at that time, which was not even understood by doctors—a gangrenous appendix.

Ephraim McDowell was something of an isolated figure in the history of medicine. He performed an "impossible" operation many times. But, though he is ranked as the Father of Abdominal Surgery, he did not have any immediate influence in his own day. The world was not yet ready for abdominal surgery as an everyday matter.

Two main problems had to be dealt with first: control of pain and control of infection. Not every patient could have Jane Crawford's inner strength, nor every surgeon Ephraim McDowell's remarkable luck. McDowell's achievements could not be repeated regularly until the development of antisepsis and anesthesia.

But he had historical importance, since his operation was the first of its kind that was ever performed successfully. And he had symbolic value too. He taught the medical profession the lesson that must be learned again and again, in every form of scientific endeavor: the lesson that the word "impossible" is no barrier to accomplishment.

9

Morton: The Defeat of Pain

CONTROL OF PAIN—that was the great challenge.

The ancient Hindu surgeons had used anesthetics such as wine, henbane, and the fumes of burning hemp. The Romans had developed various drugs for dulling the patient's senses. Opium, mandrake root, refrigeration of the body in snow—all these things were tried.

But most of the anesthetics were as bad as the pain itself. Narcotics, of course, had risks that no one realized, and many a doctor turned a patient into a drug addict in the process of sparing him from pain. The Romans tried to dull pain by bloodletting, but this usually weakened the patient past the point of simple unconsciousness, to death. Another practice, used in ancient days and revived by Paré, was applying pressure on the carotid artery in the neck, causing unconsciousness by depriving the brain of its blood supply. It should be obvious how risky that was!

By the middle of the eighteenth century, most of the painkilling techniques had been discarded as too dangerous to use, and operations were performed with the patient conscious. The situation seemed hopeless. Any painkiller strong enough to dull the patient's senses was usually too strong to permit him to survive the operation. Such harmless things as wine and whiskey did not provide any true anesthesia. Patients had a way of sobering in a hurry as the blade sliced through their flesh.

An eccentric character named Franz Mesmer offered one possible new method of anesthesia in the late eighteenth century: hypnotism. But Mesmer was a charlatan and a showman. The merits of his method were stained by the atmosphere of fraud that surrounded it. Since his time many reputable doctors have used hypnotism as an anesthetic, but it has never attained universal use.

The story of the development of modern anesthesia starts in 1772. In that year the chemist Joseph Priestly discovered nitrous oxide, or "laughing gas." Some years later, another English chemist named Humphry Davy performed some experiments with nitrous oxide. He tried some of the gas on himself, and found that it caused a pain-deadening effect, followed by unconsciousness.

In a book published in 1800, he wrote, "As nitrous oxide . . . appears capable of destroying physical pain, it may probably be used with advantage during surgical operations. . . ."

The prophetic statement went unnoticed. Surgery continued to be a nightmare profession, in which the screams of the patients haunted the sleep of the surgeons. In that pre-anesthetic age, surgeons had to work fast, slashing away hurriedly to minimize the pain of the patient. Writes Agatha Young in *Scalpel:*

> Prior to the early nineteenth century few operations lasted more than five minutes. Some surgeons could incise a bladder and remove a stone in less than sixty seconds. James Syme could whisk a leg off at the hip joint in one minute, William Ferguson used to warn the spectators not to blink or they would miss the operation altogether, and there was a popular joke about the lightning operator who could "with one sweep of his knife cut off the limb of his patient, three fingers of his assistant and the coattail of a spectator."

Relying on speed, of course, hardly improved the quality of the surgery. And some operations simply could not be rushed—which meant they were either not performed at all, or were performed in such a way as to inflict lingering torture on the patient. Many died of pain alone.

A young doctor named Henry Hill Hickman, born the same year Humphry Davy published his suggestion about the surgical use of nitrous oxide, was the next to experiment with anesthesia. This English country doctor carried out experiments in 1824, letting chickens inhale carbon dioxide. He found that the gas put the birds to sleep, and that he could perform surgery on them without apparently causing them pain.

Hickman wanted to extend his researches to larger animals. But his funds were limited. He turned to the Royal Society for a research grant, but they refused him. Strangely, the man who turned him down was that earlier experimenter with inhalation anesthesia, Humphry Davy—now *Sir* Humphry, President of the Royal Society and the dominant figure in English science. For some reason he had forgotten his own bold suggestion of 1800, and he refused to back Hickman's work. Hickman died soon after, at 30. He is remembered today only as the man who might have invented safe anesthesia, if someone had given him a chance.

"Pain in excess exhausts the principle of life," one doctor had declared. "Pain kills like hemorrhage," said another. But what could be done? How to conquer this enemy of healing?

Davy's suggestion of 1800, for surgical use of nitrous oxide, went unheeded. But nitrous oxide itself became a feature of show business.

Music hall comedians would stage demonstrations of "laughing gas." Volunteers from the audience would inhale the gas, to the great amusement of the spectators, who would watch the victims stagger around drunkenly, grow light in the head, and perform amusing antics. Sometimes an overdose would accidentally be given during these theatrical diversions. The volunteers would simply fall asleep.

Laughing-gas shows were tremendously popular, particularly in the states of the American South. Laughing-gas demonstrations even became a feature of private parties. They were called "frolics," and everyone reveled in them.

In the small Georgia town of Jefferson, the town doctor, handsome, curly-haired, 27-year-old Crawford Long, became familiar with the giddying effects of nitrous oxide and with the fumes of ether, another gas which had been found to have much the same effect. Long was asked to mix up a batch of nitrous oxide for a party that some friends of his were giving. As he himself wrote:

> In the month of December, 1841, or January, 1842, the subject of the inhalation of nitrous oxide was introduced in a company of young men assembled at night in this village (Jefferson) and several persons present desired me to prepare some for their use. I informed them that I had no apparatus for preparing or preserving the gas, but that I had a medicine (sulfuric ether) which would produce equally exhilarating effects; that I had inhaled it myself, and considered it as safe as the nitrous oxide.

The young men sampled the gas Long offered them and found that he was right. "All right," they said. "Mix us up some of that ether of yours, then!"

A series of "ether frolics" followed. The most fashionable young people of the town came to them, sniffed the gas, and went lurching gaily around, laughing uproariously. Long himself attended the frolics. He noticed that now and then one of the frolickers would trip and fall heavily, or would collide with some piece of furniture.

It was strange, Long thought, that nobody ever cried out in pain when he fell or bumped into something at an ether frolic. After one such frolic, Long noticed that he had bruised himself severely during the evening.

"When did I do that?" he wondered. "I don't remember having hurt myself."

Did the ether blank out sensations of pain, he asked himself?
Perhaps. Perhaps.

The idea had struck him that ether might have some medical use as a painkiller.

Long had a patient, a young man named James M. Venable, who

was afflicted with two small tumors on the back of his neck. "You ought to have those tumors cut out," Long had told him. "They could become dangerous."

"Well, let's do it some other time," Venable had answered. "I don't feel like being operated on just now." All too clearly, Venable was afraid of the pain surgery would involve.

Now Long went to him again. "I can remove those tumors without hurting you," he said.

"Do you mean that?"

Long smiled. "Have you ever noticed how, at an ether frolic, no one ever seems to get hurt? Ether prevents you from feeling pain. Let me give you some ether before I operate, and you'll be all right."

Venable was uneasy, but he agreed to submit. On March 30, 1842, Long poured some ether on a towel and held it over the worried Venable's mouth and nose. Venable relaxed and seemed to drop into a light sleep. Long quickly sliced away the tumors.

Slowly, Venable woke. He looked around. "When will you operate?" he asked.

"The operation is over," Long said, laughing. "See? Here are the tumors!"

Venable gaped. "No! Impossible! I felt nothing—only a slight scratch!"

Medical history was made that day in Georgia. Crawford Long carefully jotted down in his ledger, *"James Venable, 1842. Ether, and excising tumor, $2.00."*

But Long failed to publish his results. He kept the news to himself. In fact, after some of the townspeople had protested to Long that ether was poisonous and should not be used on human beings, he stopped administering it altogether.

Yet Long was the first to use ether in surgery, even if he failed at the time to see just how big a step he had taken. (Three months before, and unknown to him, a dentist named Dr. Elijah Pope, in Rochester, New York, had extracted a tooth from an etherized patient. But that was not surgery.)

In the world of science, the man who publishes his findings first gets priority for any accomplishment. Long did not choose to publish. So the honor of having been the first to use ether in surgery goes to another man—William Thomas Green Morton of Boston.

Morton was a dentist. He was born in New England in 1819 and had some idea of studying medicine. But he went in for dentistry instead and took his degree from the Baltimore College of Dental Surgery in 1842.

His involvement with anesthesia started in 1844. In that year, a Connecticut dentist named Horace Wells, who had had a shortlived partnership with Morton, went to see a nitrous-oxide show. A young man named Cooley was the subject, and he happened to injure himself while under the influence of the gas.

Although his leg was bloody, Cooley seemed to feel no pain. After the show, Wells went to the promoter and said, "It seems the gas deadens pain. Why cannot a man have a tooth extracted under the gas, and not feel it?"

"I do not know," replied the promoter, one Gardner Quincy Colton. "It never occurred to me." Colton agreed to bring a bag of nitrous oxide to Wells' office the next day for the experiment. Wells summoned a fellow dentist, John Riggs, and asked him to extract one of Wells' own wisdom teeth after administering nitrous oxide.

The tooth was pulled. When Wells returned to consciousness he declared, "It is the greatest discovery ever made! I did not feel it so much as the prick of a pin!"

Excitement gripped him. He saw a tremendous opportunity for himself. He would be the first painless puller of teeth and would make a fortune!

Wells now thought of his old partner, William Morton. When they had been practicing dentistry together, Wells and Morton had tried various painkilling methods, ranging from getting the patients drunk on brandy and champagne to giving them habit-forming narcotics like laudanum or opium.

Morton had come to see that he needed to know more about medicine in order to be a good dentist. In March, 1844, he had halted his practice and became a private medical student of Dr. Charles T. Jackson, whose name we will meet again in this chapter. After studying with Jackson for a while, Morton entered the Harvard Medical School.

Wells told Morton, "I have pulled the teeth of fifteen patients using this gas, and none of them felt any pain. Now I want to demonstrate the gas in front of doctors!"

Since Morton was a medical student, Wells used him as a contact with the world of medicine. Through Morton, Wells arranged that a demonstration of nitrous oxide anesthesia would be given at the Massachusetts General Hospital before a class in surgery.

But the demonstration was a fiasco. Either the student who volunteered to be the patient had an abnormal resistance to nitrous oxide, or else the anesthetic was not administered properly. In any event, the patient bellowed in pain as Wells yanked the tooth.

Cries of "Humbug! Humbug!" echoed in the lecture hall. Wells fled in dismay.

Morton, though, grew deeply interested in the whole problem of anesthesia. He went to his old teacher, Charles T. Jackson, and discussed Wells' findings with him.

Jackson was a chemist as well as a doctor. He was a keen-witted but sly and unscrupulous man. He was nicknamed "the scientific octopus," because he had tried to claim priority in several important discoveries of the time. Among other things, Jackson insisted that he, and not Samuel F. B. Morse, had invented the telegraph, and that Morse had stolen the idea from him.

Morton knew something of Jackson's reputation and tried not to let him in on much of what was really going on. At first, Morton simply wanted to borrow experimental apparatus from Jackson.

But Jackson realized something special was underway. He asked question after question until Morton finally admitted he was doing anesthesia research with nitrous oxide.

"Nitrous oxide is too undependable," Jackson said. "I would advise you to try sulphuric ether instead."

Morton went back to Wells with the word that Jackson did not favor nitrous oxide. Wells, though, stuck to his original idea, and from then on he and Morton went their separate ways. Wells continued to use nitrous oxide on his own patients. But Morton started to experiment with ether.

For eighteen months Morton experimented—on his own spaniel, first, and then on the family goldfish, on caterpillars, and finally on himself. He did little else but experiment with ether. His medical studies all but ceased, and what was left of his dental practice had to be handed over to other men. This is how Morton described his own experience with ether:

> I shut myself up in my room; seated myself in the operating chair and commenced inhaling. . . . It partially suffocated me but produced no decided effect. I then saturated my handkerchief and inhaled from that. I looked at my watch and soon lost consciousness. As I recovered I felt a numbness in my limbs with a sensation like a nightmare and would have given the world for some one to come and arouse me. I thought for a moment I should die. . . . At length I felt a slight tingling of the blood in the end of my third finger and made an effort to touch it with my thumb, but without success. At a second effort I touched it, but there seemed to be no sensation. . . . I pinched my thigh, but . . . sensation was imperfect. . . . I immediately looked at my watch. . . . I had been insensible between seven and eight minutes.

This was on September 30, 1846. Later that same day, a patient called on Morton, one Eben Frost, suffering from toothache. Morton painlessly pulled the aching tooth after having given Frost ether.

The story from here on becomes hopelessly tangled. Claims and counterclaims render the tale a knotty one. Somehow—through much intrigue and machination—Morton persuaded Dr. John Collins Warren of the Massachusetts General Hospital to make experimental use of ether in surgery.

Dr. Warren was the same man who had sponsored the Wells tooth-pulling fiasco in 1845. How Morton, a 27-year-old medical student, was able to talk the austere Dr. Warren into taking a second look at anesthetic gases, we will never know.

But Morton succeeded. Warren invited him to come to the hospital on October 16, 1846, to administer his anesthetic to a patient named Gilbert Abbott, who was to be operated on for a large tumor at the side of his neck.

Morton was fifteen minutes late for the operation. It seems he was waiting for a newly designed ether inhaler to be finished that very morning. When Dr. Warren, a tall, dignified man of 68, one of the leading surgeons of his time, entered the operating theater, he looked around and remarked, "As Dr. Morton has not arrived, I presume he is otherwise engaged." Quite likely he thought Morton had backed out at the last minute, rather than fail with ether as Wells had failed with nitrous oxide.

Warren picked up his scalpel to begin.

But then the young dentist burst into the room, carrying the glass inhaler that had been completed only a few minutes before. Warren nodded to him, and Morton proceeded to prepare his inhaler, saturating a sponge in ether and enclosing it in the glass globe.

"Well, sir!" Warren said. "Your patient is ready." There was a touch of sarcasm in his voice.

Morton approached the operating table, where the patient was strapped down, according to usual procedure. Morton pointed across the room to Eben Frost, his earlier successful patient. "There is a man who has breathed the preparation and can testify to its success," Morton said.

Frost nodded to Abbott, who looked somewhat pale.

"Are you afraid?" Morton asked the patient.

"No," Abbott gamely replied. "I feel confident and will do precisely as you tell me."

Morton gave him the inhaler, putting the tube in his lips. Abbott breathed in and out. His face grew flushed, and his arms and legs jerked for a moment or two. Within four minutes, he was unconscious. Morton turned proudly to Warren and bowed to the surgeon.

"Sir, *your* patient is ready," he said.

Warren operated amid tense silence. The familiar screams of the patient were absent. Abbott showed no sign of awareness. Swiftly, Warren cut out the tumor and stitched the incision. Profoundly moved, he looked up to the watching students and declared, "Gentlemen, this is no humbug."

A new era in surgery had opened.

As Warren later wrote, "The surgeon's visitations on the most delicate parts now are performed, not only without the agonizing screams he has been accustomed to hear, but sometimes in a state of perfect insensibility, and, occasionally, even with an expression of pleasure on the part of the patient. . . . If Ambroise Paré, and Louis, and Dessault, and Cheselden, and Hunter, and Cooper, could see what our eyes daily witness, how they would long to come among us, and perform their exploits once more!"

But Morton was infected with the money-making germ. He promptly applied for a patent on his "discovery," and got it on November 12, 1846. To protect his rights, he had refused to disclose to anyone, even Warren, just what the substance in the inhaler was. He had given it the name of "Letheon," and tried to disguise the ether odor with aromatic oils. Anyone at all could prepare ether. Morton hoped that he would make a fortune by selling the mysterious "Letheon" to hospitals.

The story becomes a sordid one now. Morton's unethical attempt to patent a healing technique for his own private profit led him into debt and bitter controversy. A patent is only a license to sue. As soon as others found out that "Letheon" was only ether, many surgeons began using it, and Morton tried to sue them all. He bankrupted himself in the attempt.

And Charles Jackson, "the scientific octopus," now stepped in and tried to get a patent himself. He announced—truly—that he had been the one to suggest to Morton the use of ether instead of nitrous oxide. Jackson, experienced in the ways of such disputes, soon had half the world thinking that he was the man behind the great discovery and that Morton had merely carried out his instructions.

Saddest of all was Horace Wells, who had put both men onto the idea. Wells now convinced himself that he had been experimenting with ether as well as nitrous oxide all along, and so he, not Morton or Jackson, deserved the credit! In desperation he tried to improve on ether by experimenting with yet another painkilling drug, chloroform. But he handled the drug poorly, and became addicted to it. His final days were spent in madness, and on January 24, 1848, he was found with his throat cut and an empty bottle of chloroform at his feet.

This left only Jackson and Morton to contend for the honor of discovering the surgical uses of ether—or so it seemed. But now, out of Georgia, came the claim of Crawford Long to have used ether on James Venable, four years before the Morton-Warren operation on Gilbert Abbott!

The issue was thoroughly confused. A congressional investigation followed. Everyone seemed to agree that Long really did have priority, but his mysterious failure to publish his findings robbed him of any claim to credit. What about Jackson and Morton, though?

Morton had bankrupted himself in legal expenses. Now he went to the United States Congress and asked for a grant of $100,000, as a reward for his services to humanity. Congress bickered over it for eight years. Every time it seemed that Morton would be voted the money, up jumped Jackson with his conflicting claims. Congress never voted anything. The French Institute, though, voted an award of 5,000 francs, divided equally between Jackson and Morton.

Morton and Jackson continued to dispute for many years. In the end, Morton was penniless and professionally discredited, and died in 1869, an embittered, exhausted man. Jackson, broken by the long quarrel, went insane in 1873 and dragged out the final seven years of his life in an asylum. And Wells, of course, died young, a suicide.

The controversy over the discovery of ether anesthesia was one of the sensations of the nineteenth century. Today, long after tempers have cooled, we can attribute the honors this way:

Crawford Long was undoubtedly the first man to use ether in surgery. But Long never followed up his idea, never sought to introduce it as general surgical technique, and so does not rate cerdit for a medical innovation. The man responsible for the introduction of ether anesthesia is Morton, who based his work on suggestions from Wells and Jackson.

Only one item of credit is really certain. That is the name of the man who coined the word "anesthesia." He was Oliver Wendell Holmes, the poet and physician, who wrote to Morton on November 21, 1846:

> Everybody wants to have a hand in a great discovery. All I will do is to give you a hint or two, as to names or the name to be applied to the state produced and the agent.
>
> The state should, I think, be called "Anaesthesia." This signifies insensibility, more particularly . . . to objects of touch. Thus we might say, the state of anaesthesia or the anæsthetic state. . . .
>
> I would have a name pretty soon, and consult some accomplished scholar . . . before fixing upon the terms, which will be repeated by the tongues of every civilized race of mankind. . . .

The maze of conflicting claims is of no real importance to anyone but the men involved. Ether, though, *was* of importance. Surgery was revolutionized. Anesthesia was firmly established as a part of surgical technique. No longer would it be necessary to strap patients to the table. No longer would a surgeon's dreams ring with patients' shrieks.

Other anesthetics soon joined ether. In England, James Young Simpson experimented with chloroform as an anesthetic and found it in many ways more useful than ether. Cocaine, morphine, novocaine, and a host of other drugs came into use soon after.

Of course, the early days of anesthesia were not without their setbacks. Cocaine and morphine proved to be habit-forming. But this fact was not discovered until many patients had become addicts. Ether turned out to have harmful side-effects when not administered properly. The techniques of anesthesia needed and got steady refinement all through the nineteenth century.

Today, anesthesia is a complex branch of medicine, and its techniques require the presence of a specially trained person at most operations. The miracles of modern anesthesia would baffle a Crawford Long or a William Morton and then would cause delight and amazement.

Out of the ugly, twisted Morton-Jackson-Wells-Long controversy came the solution to one of medicine's biggest problems: control of pain. Attention now had to turn toward the next great challenge, that of controlling infection.

10

Lister: The Defeat of Infection

I<small>T WAS</small> a wine merchant's son named Joseph Lister who completed the revolution in the operating room. Morton and the others had banished pain. Lister banished that other dread menace, infection.

It is hard for us to believe that doctors once failed to draw the connection between dirt and disease. It seems so obvious to us, but only because we live after Lister's day. Try to accept this picture of the medical profession in the days of our great-great-great-grandfathers:

Cleanliness is regarded as a nuisance. Overworked doctors and hospital workers cannot bother with such trivia as using clean linens and unsoiled instruments.

No one understands the nature of pus. Doctors praise it, calling it "laudable pus"—a sign that a wound is draining properly, that all will be well. Pus is common and expected. In fact, if a wound shows signs of healing without it, the doctor often applies irritating dressings that will bring about the development of pus.

But it is not often that this step must be taken. Pus, infection, these are present universally. And small wonder. A surgeon comes to the operating room straight from the anatomy lab, where he has been lecturing to students and handling dead bodies. He dons a filthy operating jacket to work in, caked with the blood and pus of earlier patients. He seizes the knife in his unwashed hands. Perhaps he sharpens it on

117

a dirty barber's strop. He bends over the patient, who is also unwashed, and who lies on a plain wooden table. A ring of assistants stands around, and perhaps half a dozen students as well. Everyone is breathing openly into the surgical incision as they bend for a closer view.

Infection, of course, is almost unavoidable. Sometimes the infection is relatively mild. The wound fills with pus, and the patient's temperature rises, but nothing worse happens, and in a few days the pus drains away.

But often the temperature rise is sudden and sharp. The wound swells and throbs. The patient dies of blood poisoning. John Bell, a surgeon who lived before Lister's revolution, gives us this chilling description of blood poisoning after an incision in the leg:

> The great wound begins to open very wide, the whole limb swells to an enormous degree. . . . You are aware that great suppurations are forming within. . . . Often it happens that all your cares are unavailing. Every time you make an examination of the limb you make discoveries of more extensive destruction, you find the whole limb swelling more and more, you find the matter running profusely from the openings. . . . And in the end . . . the hollow eyes . . . the long, bony fingers . . . the quick, short breathing and the small piping voice declare the last stages. . . .

We realize today that there are many kinds of infection. But in that uncomplicated era only three types of blood poisoning were known: pyemia, erysipelas, and "hospital gangrene," the worst of the three. All three were usually fatal. So James Simpson, the pioneer of chloroform anesthesia, could write in the middle of the last century, "A man laid on the operating table in one of our surgical hospitals is exposed to more chances of death than the English soldier on the field of Waterloo!"

Doctors feared blood poisoning greatly, and took what they hoped were steps to prevent it. But without any clear understanding of what caused infection, there was no way of fighting it.

The fourteenth-century surgeon Guy de Chauliac said, "A surgeon who does not know his anatomy is like a blind man hewing a log." Just so, surgeons who did not know how infection started had no way of dealing with it. They could only guess. In ancient days, wine had been used to cleanse wounds. Later, whitewash was considered valuable, and hospital walls were regularly swabbed with it.

It was vaguely thought that small creatures in the bloodstream had something to do with infection. But how did they get there? Aristotle had taught that germlike creatures arose from spontaneous causes, generated of their own accord. If that was so, there was no means of guarding against them. They could spontaneously arise anywhere, like phantoms coming through the walls of the strongest fortress.

A few doctors at the beginning of the nineteenth century guessed dimly at the connection between dirt and disease. One surgeon started to treat infected wounds with chloride of lime. Another in Marseilles told all doctors to wash their hands in a chlorine solution before operating. But few listened.

Still the patients died regularly in the congested, filthy hospitals. If a patient broke a limb and the bone pierced the skin, it was thought safer to amputate than to set the limb, since there was less danger of infection that way. But a third to a half of all amputations ended in death of infection anyway.

One tragic cause of death in women was puerperal fever, an infection that strikes just after childbirth. Doctors with dirty hands brought death to thousands of young mothers in those days. Epidemics of the fever were commonplace.

In 1795, two English doctors identified puerperal fever as the same kind of infection as hospital gangrene, and proved that it was caused by contagion.

"Ridiculous! Absurd!" older doctors sputtered. "Puerperal fever contagious? Nonsense!"

But then, in 1843, a young American doctor named Oliver Wendell

Holmes published a short paper called *The Contagiousness of Puerperal Fever*. Forcefully written, splendidly documented, it has become a medical classic. Holmes was violently attacked by his seniors, who realized that if he was right, they were little more than murderers. Holmes replied:

> When, by the permission of Providence, I held up to the professional public the damnable facts connected with the conveyance of poison from one young mother's chamber to another's—for doing which humble office I desire to be thankful that I have lived, though nothing else should ever come to my life—I had to bear the sneers of those whose position I had assailed, and, as I believe, have at last demolished, so that nothing but the ghosts of dead women stir among the ruins.

Soon after Holmes wrote this, an Austrian doctor named Ignaz Philipp Semmelweis (1818–1865) was becoming concerned with the high mortality rate from puerperal fever. It stunned and shocked him. Serving as an assistant at the Allgemeines Krankenhaus, the great maternity hospital of Vienna, Semmelweis noticed something odd: that in one ward of the hospital, childbed mortality ran from 12 to 30 percent, while in another ward—which was set aside for the training of midwives—no more than 3 percent of the young mothers died.

Everyone knew this. Pregnant women turned pale with fright when they were assigned to the high-mortality ward. But no one knew why one ward was so much safer than the other.

"Atmospheric differences," one expert said. "Cosmic influences," said another. "Overcrowding in one ward," said a third. While another opined that the women in the high-mortality ward died of emotional strain because they were examined by male students. A step was taken: Foreign students were barred from the death ward, because they were thought "rougher" than the Viennese. But still the deaths mounted.

The sensitive and gentle Semmelweis was as puzzled as anyone else. But in 1847, Semmelweis' friend, Dr. Kolletschka, died of blood poisoning after a clumsy medical student had pricked Kolletschka's finger during a dissection of a dead victim of puerperal fever. Semmelweis immediately saw that some material from the dead woman's body must have been transmitted to poor Kolletschka's finger by the dissecting scalpel.

Now it was clear!

In the high-mortality ward, the women were attended by medical students who went straight from the dissecting lab to the childbeds. The students examined the women without washing their hands—and carried on their hands some deadly substance picked up while dissecting the bodies of the recent victims of puerperal disease! In the other ward, where midwives who did not practice dissection handled the mothers, mortality was far lower.

Hand-washing was the answer, Semmelweis proclaimed. "It is owing to the doctors that there is so high a mortality in childbed! God only knows how many women I have prematurely brought down into the grave!"

He launched a determined campaign. Everyone who examined a patient, every doctor, every student, had to wash his hands in chlorine before approaching the ward. The death rate in Semmelweis' ward dropped almost to zero. But when he tried to get other hospitals to adopt his methods, he hit trouble. What did this young doctor know? It was only coincidence, he was told, that deaths were dropping in his ward. Medical men did not have time to waste in foolish handwashing!

No one would listen. Semmelweis became angry and impassioned. "Murder must cease!" he cried. He told one famous German doctor, "I proclaim you before God and the world to be an assassin!"

His wild attacks left him open to laughter and scorn. His mind became clouded, and he lapsed into insanity for a while. Finally, like his friend Kolletschka, he died of blood poisoning after cutting himself during an operation. He was only 47.

Semmelweis is a tragic figure. But his discovery was important.

Before long, doctors everywhere would honor him. In his own time, though, he met only with contempt.

Semmelweis had found something basic: that cleaning the hands before examining a recent mother would reduce the risk of puerperal fever. But he did not know *why*.

The *why* was then being worked out by a French chemist—not a medical doctor at all—named Louis Pasteur. Pasteur had begun to do research into the fermentation of alcohol in 1854. Ten years later, a group of winemakers hired him. "Our wine is spoiling," they said. "Tell us how we can prevent it!"

Pasteur found that bacteria in the wine were souring it. "Heat the wine a short while," Pasteur told them. "It will kill the little organisms that live in it." The process of disinfecting by heating, *pasteurization,* resulted. And Pasteur also found, by microscopic examination, that bacteria reproduced by dividing in two. The old theory of spontaneous generation was exploded.

Pasteur's research formed the foundation stone of modern bacteriology. It remained for the English surgeon Joseph Lister (1827–1912) to apply Pasteur's findings to the problems of the hospital.

Lister was born into a Quaker family. His father, a wealthy wine merchant, was a cultured, scientifically-inclined man whose hobby was the microscope. Lister early learned the methods of science from his father.

He grew up shy, a stammerer, a quiet boy. Medicine was his choice of profession. Because he was a Quaker, he was a victim of religious discrimination. Instead of going to one of the more famous schools, he enrolled at University College of London, where Friends were treated well. There, as a freshman medical student, he had the good luck to watch an operation of historical importance: the first major operation done under ether in England.

The surgeon was Robert Liston. At the start of the operation Liston announced, "We are going to try a Yankee dodge today, gentlemen, for making men insensible."

Young Lister was fascinated. It was December, 1846, only two months after Morton and Warren had made their pioneering operation in Boston. From that moment on, Lister felt that he was destined for a career in surgery.

During his medical school days, he became aware of the problem of infection after surgery. He studied cases of gangrene, scraping the gray matter from wounds and pondering it under his microscope. But he could draw no conclusions.

In 1852, he took his medical degree and moved on to Scotland. There, the soft-spoken Englishman became assistant to James Syme, professor of clinical surgery at Edinburgh. Syme, a painstaking, conservative surgeon, had an outstanding reputation. And, though he was nicknamed "The Formidable" and was supposed to be hard to get along with, he took an immediate liking to young Lister.

Lister and Syme formed a fine surgical team. Lister's abilities grew. But he had no great opinion of himself. He wrote his father from Edinburgh:

> I am encouraged to hope that, though I must not expect to be a Liston or a Syme, still I shall get on. Certain it is I love surgery more and more, and this is one great point. . . . As to brilliant talent, I know I do not possess it, but I must try to make up as far as I can by perseverance.

Lister persevered. In 1854, Lister was appointed a lecturer at the medical school. Two years later, he asked for the hand of Syme's daughter. The old surgeon was happy to see her married to his favorite protégé. Lister had to leave the Quakers, though, and become an Anglican in order to wed Agnes Syme. She was serious, intellectual, rather shy, not particularly good-looking—a person very much like Lister himself.

He went into private practice, but made little money at it. To support himself and his bride, Lister in 1860 took a post as professor of surgery at the University of Glasgow.

Working in Syme's infirmary at Edinburgh, Lister had had plenty of opportunity to see gangrene at work. Syme insisted on cleanliness in his wards, and used dry dressings rather than wet ones soaked in unsterilized water. Nonetheless, gangrene was common. In the bleak wards of the dismal Glasgow hospital to which Lister now went, conditions were far less sanitary, and the death rate from gangrene and other infections was appalling.

Lister made a few changes in the Glasgow procedure. He put in a big order for soap and towels. The older doctors grumbled. "More of this hand-washing foolishness!" they complained.

Even so, patients died—more than half of those who came under the knife. It was a depressing business. Why labor to operate, only to lose the patient more often than not?

Lister pondered the matter of amputations. One fact glared at him. In simple fractures, where the skin is not broken, there almost never was infection. In compound fractures, in which a jagged end of bone protrudes through the skin, there almost always was.

Doctors were so used to this state of affairs that they automatically amputated in any case of compound fracture. Better to lop the limb off, they felt, than to set it and risk blood poisoning. Even so, the amputated stump would become gangrenous at least a third of the time. It struck Lister that whenever the skin was broken—whether through compound fracture or by the surgeon's knife—infection was the result.

"Why?" he wondered. "Why is it always this way?"

Obviously, something in the air caused infection. "Oxygen," declared many doctors gravely. "There's the villain! Oxygen!" Since there was no way of keeping oxygen from coming into contact with a raw surface during surgery, it was clear that infection was unpreventable.

Lister would not buy this theory. Why should oxygen be a cause of infection? Where was the proof?

Lister pondered, and still the patients died. Lister began to suspect that whatever caused the infection did not eat away from outside, as oxygen was supposed to do, but corroded from within. All the evidence pointed to the fact that infection began deep in the wound.

In 1865, Lister discussed the whole problem of infection with Thomas Anderson, professor of chemistry at Glasgow.

"Take this book," Anderson said. "It may give you some ideas."

It was a copy of Pasteur's famous paper, *Recherches sur la putrefaction,* "Research into Infection." In that simple way, Thomas Anderson won immortality for himself, for he served as the catalyst that meshed the ideas of Pasteur with those of Lister.

Pasteur had proved that the atmosphere was full of microorganisms, microbes that swarmed in the air. These microbes were the causes of fermentation and putrefaction.

Lister was thunderstuck. Of course! Every operating room was full of microbes! They must hover in clouds in the air, must cluster on every table, every gown, every scalpel. And when the surgeon's knife laid bare raw flesh, or when a compound fracture broke the skin, the microbes hastened to enter the body, to dwell and multiply, and to devour the healthy tissues!

Lister saw the answer. First the surgeon should cleanse the wound of all microbes. Then he should seal the wound, so that nothing could enter to infect during the period of healing. Sepsis—infection—was the great enemy. Lister set out to develop techniques of *antisepsis*.

Pasteur recommended boiling to kill microbes. But living patients could hardly be pasteurized. Some other means—some chemical means—had to be found.

Lister experimented with chloride of zinc and with various sulphites, but found them unsatisfactory. Then, one day, strolling the banks of the Eden River in the town of Carlisle, he came upon a municipal sewage plant. A thick, oily substance called German creosote was used as the purifying agent.

"What is this creosote?" he asked his chemist friend, Anderson.

"An impure form of carbolic acid," Anderson said. "Carbolic acid is often used for purifying sewage that way."

Lister got a sample of carbolic acid from Anderson. It was not the clear, thin substance we know today, but rather a dark, molasseslike, foul-smelling fluid.

In March, 1865, Lister received a patient on whom he decided to try his new theory of antisepsis. He was an elderly factory worker with a compound fracture of the leg. The man seemed too weak to survive an amputation. But infection would certainly carry him off if the leg were not removed.

Lister coated the wound with carbolic acid and set the leg. But the man died of the shock of his accident, neither proving nor disproving Lister's theory.

Two months later, Lister had a second patient. He was James Greenless, a boy of eleven who had been run over by a cart. His leg was fractured and the bone had pierced the skin. Lister saturated a piece of lint in carbolic acid and placed it over the wound. Then he set the leg and applied another dressing. On the fourth day—the day when infection usually began—Lister fearfully lifted the dressing, half expecting to find the wound oozing pus.

The wound was covered with a scab. There was no pus, no sign of infection. The only discomfort the boy felt was in places where the carbolic acid, applied undiluted, had burned the skin.

Lister rejoiced at his success. "But one case proves nothing," he told himself. "I must try others."

Over the next eighteen months, he used his antiseptic treatment on eleven more patients. Of these, one died. Two developed gangrene, but recovered, one needing amputation, the other not requiring it. The other eight patients recovered without complications.

Lister published his findings in March, 1867, in the British medical journal, *The Lancet,* under the title, "On a new Method of Treating Compound Fracture, etc." Of course, only a handful of cases were involved, thirteen in all. But two deaths out of thirteen was far below the old average. And seven of his cases had involved severe skin lacerations, which once had been almost automatically fatal.

Lister's first article did not make clear *why* carbolic acid worked. Later that same year he wrote a second paper, "On the Antiseptic

Principle in the Practice of Surgery," to make it clear that his treatment was based on the need to keep microbes out of open wounds.

During the next few years, Lister and other surgeons throughout Europe conducted further experiments with the antiseptic method. One thing they quickly learned was that carbolic acid was a risky substance to use, in its undiluted form. Lister's early patients had been lucky to escape severe burns and carbolic acid poisoning. Soon it was realized that the acid had to be diluted to a tenth or even a twentieth of its normal strength for safe use.

There were problems. Many doctors, tempted to see how the wound was coming along, would peek under the dressing, letting new microbes in. Lister himself didn't fully comprehend the nature of infection at first, either, and failed to see that, while carbolic acid could prevent fresh wounds from being infected, it was not as useful in sterilizing already-infected wounds. And so there were many failures in the early years of antisepsis.

Lister's idea that the exclusion of air from the wound was important was only partly true, also. While many of the bacteria were air-dwellers, some, such as those of tetanus ("lockjaw") and gas gangrene, did not need air for life. No degree of sealing the wound could guard against these *anerobic* microorganisms.

Still, the impact of Lister's ideas was great. But there were the usual attacks and objections from the old guard. Doctors who had just barely come to see the value of soap and water could not go on to embrace carbolic acid dressings as well. But as the death rate dropped in hospitals where Lister's methods were practiced, the clamor against antisepsis died away.

Lister extended his researches. He developed an antiseptic treatment for abscesses as well as amputations. He studied the types of ligatures then in use for tying off blood vessels, and concluded that ligatures of silk, whipcord, or silver wire caused infection and pain. He suggested using catgut ligatures—actually made from the intestines of sheep—which would be gradually absorbed by the body. Though not the inventor of catgut ligatures, he made their use popular.

He still felt that the chief danger was infection from the air. He was right in this, but carried his thinking to an extreme. In 1870, he invented an odd device that would spray a 2 percent solution of carbolic acid into the atmosphere of the dressing room. Undoubtedly this spray killed all bacteria in the vicinity. But it also drenched the surgeon and his assistants, chapped exposed skin, and sometimes harmed the patient.

For a while the carbolic acid spray was very fashionable. Lister even used it when Queen Victoria was operated on for an abscess in 1871. To Her Majesty's annoyance, Lister's assistant squirted some of the carbolic acid into the royal eye. But no damage was done.

In 1880, a German surgeon, Viktor von Brunn, demolished the use of the spray with a sarcastic pamphlet. It fell into disuse at once. Lister himself stopped using the spray in 1887.

Lister also improved the design of the dressing he used. Now, after an operation, he would cover the wound with gauze, eightfold thick, drenched in carbolic acid, liquid resin, and paraffin. A piece of mackintosh sheeting was placed between the layers of gauze, and a sheet of waxed taffeta over everything.

In 1869, Lister had replaced his father-in-law, Syme, as professor of surgery at Edinburgh. Eight years later he left Scotland to take up the same post at King's College, London. Medicine in London was still dominated by conservatives who opposed Lister's ideas. He looked on the London assignment as a personal challenge.

He was startled by the state of the surgical art in London. All through Europe, antisepsis was acclaimed, but in London an almost medieval attitude prevailed. Little by little, Lister won London over. His fame spread.

Though he was now acclaimed as the greatest surgeon in Great Britain, he still went through his wards himself, stopping to talk with every patient, no matter how humble. Once he came upon a weeping little girl in one ward.

"You seem to be doing well," Lister said. "Why are you crying?"

"The nurse took my doll away. There was a hole in it, and the sawdust came out and got into the bed."

"Perhaps I can heal your doll's wound," Lister said. Smiling, the great surgeon sent for the doll, and carefully stitched up the hole as though he were operating on the Queen.

Honors came to Lister as the years went by. In 1883 he was knighted. Nine years later, he retired from teaching, but not from medicine. He was elected President of the Royal Society in 1895, and two years afterward became Lord Lister, the first medical man to be raised to the English peerage. He died at the age of 85 in 1912, honored and beloved throughout the world, and the greatest men of the medical profession paid homage to him at Westminster Abbey.

Although he did not know of the work of Semmelweis until late in his own life, Lister was responsible for the fulfillment of Semmelweis' dream. Semmelweis had not known why it was important to cleanse the hands in a chemical solution; he only knew that it helped. Lister, making use of Pasteur's ideas, not only showed why antisepsis was necessary, but developed practical techniques that saved millions of lives.

Lister's concept of antisepsis has since given way to the notion of *asepsis*—that is, destroying bacteria before they can reach the wound, rather than afterward. Lister himself was tending toward asepsis when he recommended soaking surgical instruments in carbolic acid.

Today, carbolic acid is a relic of medicine's past. In the 1880's, German surgeons introduced the boiling of instruments and then the steam sterilizer. Other antiseptics have replaced carbolic in the inevitable march of medical progress.

It is hard for us to envision the pre-antisepsis era now. How many friends of yours have broken arms or legs while skiing or playing football? Think of all the casts you have autographed—and then stop to realize that a hundred years ago, nearly all those broken limbs would have had to be amputated, and half the victims would never have left the hospital alive. It is chilling to imagine that army of legless and armless people, those rows of graves. Think of the cases of appendicitis you have known about—and consider that a hundred years ago almost every case would have ended fatally. It seems miraculous that anyone survived to adulthood at all in those times.

With Lister's revolution, the last barrier to surgical progress was down. Vesalius had ended the period of anatomical ignorance. Harvey's findings had helped other doctors discover how to control bleeding. Morton and Long had freed the patient from pain. And now Lister had lifted a shining shield against infection. A brave new world of medicine was coming into being, as the nineteenth century drew to its close.

11

Reed: "I Leave So Little!"

MANY of the great doctors we have met thus far were surgeons. Paré, John Hunter, McDowell, Lister—they were all wielders of the knife. In those years before the causes of disease were really understood, surgery was the branch of medicine that grew most rapidly. Plagues could not be dealt with until men knew why they arose, but tumors could be cut out, limbs amputated.

Late in the nineteenth century, a change in emphasis occurs. The ideas of Pasteur put mention of microbes on everyone's lips. For the first time, men can begin to probe the mysteries of disease. And, gradually, the dreaded epidemic killers—malaria, yellow fever, typhoid, and the rest of that grim crew—start to drop back before the onslaught of the doctors.

Of these killers, one of the most fearsome was yellow fever, or "yellow jack." It was a disease of the New World. Christopher Columbus, on his second journey across the Atlantic, planted a colony on Hispaniola, the island that today is divided between Haiti and the Dominican Republic. His men sickened; their skins turned yellow; they died. Later, Napoleon Bonaparte sent an expeditionary force to Haiti; the yellow fever wiped it out.

Through the West Indies, Central America, South America, the disease raged in epidemic after terrible epidemic. In Colonial days, it

131

killed 100,000 Americans. During the fever season, southerly places like Florida, Texas, and Louisiana were danger zones. Along the Mississippi, watchful men kept "shotgun quarantines" to prevent yellow fever carriers from coming north out of epidemic areas. Although it was basically a tropical disease, yellow jack sometimes struck in the north, as far as New York. A month-long epidemic in Philadelphia in 1793 wiped out a tenth of the city's people.

Today yellow jack is little more than an ugly memory. The man we honor as its vanquisher is Virginia-born Dr. Walter Reed. But Reed was one of a group of men who combined their efforts to defeat the yellow fever menace. We have to look at Reed's accomplishment against the background of other achievements by many other men.

The first of these was a Cuban doctor of French and Scottish descent, Carlos Finlay. Trained as a doctor in France and in Philadelphia, Dr. Finlay was a familiar figure in Havana, always immaculate in his white suit, generally puffing on a fine Havana cigar. He was a charming, witty man, fond of good wine and good conversation.

Carlos Finlay was troubled by Cuba's tragic affliction of yellow fever. Thousands of Cubans each year came down with the disease, and half its victims died. Finlay studied the history of yellow fever. He concluded that it had originated in the Western Hemisphere and had somehow traveled to tropical areas throughout the world. But how?

In 1880, a French doctor named Laveran had demonstrated that another disease, malaria, was transmitted by mosquitoes. Finlay wondered if it were the same with yellow fever. In February, 1881, at a meeting of the International Sanitary Conference in Washington, D.C., Finlay made the blunt statement: "Yellow fever is carried by mosquitoes!" But he had no proof. It was only a theory.

For the next six months, back in Cuba, Finlay followed his theory with research. He caught all sorts of mosquitoes, kept them in test tubes, studied their breeding habits. He paid particular attention to mosquitoes found hovering around yellow fever victims. Finlay captured some of these mosquitoes and found volunteers who would let themselves be bitten by them. Six of the volunteers came down with yellow fever!

In August, 1881, Finlay made an even more definite announcement. Not only was he certain that mosquitoes carried yellow fever, but he could name the mosquito! It was the stegomyia mosquito, with the scientific name *Aedes aegypti.*

The way to stamp out yellow fever, Finlay said, was to wipe out the stegomyia mosquito. Destroy its breeding places and the disease would vanish. But no one listened. He was laughed at. People called him the "mosquito doctor." They said the tropical heat had addled his brains. He slipped into oblivion, his theories all but forgotten as the years passed.

Now it was 1898. The Spanish-American War flared up and raged briefly. American soldiers poured into Cuba, then a Spanish possession. The Spanish bullets were badly aimed, but the sting of the mosquito was more accurate. More Americans died of yellow fever during the war than of battle wounds.

The war ended in less than a year. An American army of occupation moved in, taking control of the island until an independent Cuban republic could be set up. General Leonard Wood, who had a medical background, was the commanding officer. General Wood knew that the United States soldiers would be driven from the island by fever unless yellow jack could be halted.

"Clean up Havana!" he ordered. "We'll establish sanitary conditions here!"

The city was scrubbed. As though to mock the scrubbers, yellow fever climbed to its highest peak in two decades. Sanitation was not the answer.

What was?

Who knew?

General Wood needed answers, fast. More than a third of the officers on his own staff had perished of yellow jack. He cabled

Washington for help. The Federal Government appointed a commission of four men to go to Cuba and investigate yellow fever.

One of the four was a Cuban, Aristides Agramonte. He had had yellow fever and survived, so he was immune. It would be his job to dissect the bodies of the dead fever victims. The second member of the commission was Dr. James Carroll, an army surgeon. The third was Dr. Jesse Lazear, a European-trained bacteriologist. The fourth, the head of the Yellow Fever Commission, was Dr. Walter Reed, professor of bacteriology in the Army Medical School.

Reed was the son of a Methodist minister. Born in 1851, he was not quite 49 when the Commission arrived in Cuba in June, 1900. He had taken his first medical degree at the University of Virginia when he was just seventeen, then had taken another from Bellevue Medical College in New York. At 22, he was an inspector of the Brooklyn Board of Health.

He had gone from there into the Medical Corps of the U.S. Army. He spent eighteen years in military outposts all over the country, mostly in Indian territory in the far west. Transferred to a post in Baltimore, he was able to take special courses in bacteriology and pathology at the brand-new but already famous Johns Hopkins Medical School of that city. When the Spanish-American War broke out, Reed, now professor of bacteriology himself at the Army Medical School, had the task of dealing with the epidemics of typhoid fever in army medical camps. His research showed that the common fly was the carrier of typhoid, and he was instrumental in coping with that disease.

Now a far more fearsome disease was the foe. When the Commission arrived in Cuba, the yellow jack epidemic was at its worst. The dead and the dying lay everywhere. The city was spotless, and for the first time in its history had adequate sewers, but still the disease raged, and it seemed that the American army faced certain doom.

The commissioners performed autopsies on eighteen yellow jack victims. They could not find a single suspicious microbe. All during sweltering July they labored over their cadavers, to no avail. They were stymied.

Walter Reed had heard of the "mosquito doctor," Carlos Finlay, and his theories of 1881. Finlay was regarded as a harmless crank, an old eccentric. But the commissioners could leave no avenue unexplored. Reed went to see Finlay.

"This is the culprit," Finlay told him. "The stegomyia mosquito."

He showed Reed specimens of the stegomyia, with its silver-striped belly and white-striped legs. He gave Reed eggs of the stegomyia, and explained how the mosquito liked to breed in stagnant water, usually in towns rather than the country.

Reed nurtured the eggs. Stegomyia mosquitoes hatched. The logical next step was to perform experiments on animals, to see if the mosquitoes really could transmit yellow fever.

But no known animals were susceptible to yellow jack. Only humans seemed to contract it. The guinea pigs for the experiment would have to be human beings. But who?

"We must begin with ourselves," the commissioners decided. They felt that they had no right to experiment on others.

James Carroll was the first to submit. Some of the stegomyias were taken to a yellow fever ward and allowed to bite several patients. Then Carroll allowed the mosquitoes to bite him. Lazear and Agramonte also permitted themselves to be bitten. Reed would have submitted too, but he was called back to Washington to deliver an official report.

When he returned from Washington soon afterward, tragic news awaited him. In the original experiments, only Carroll had contracted yellow fever. For several days he hovered on the brink of death, but then recovered. Agramonte and Lazear had not developed the disease. But then, a short time later, Lazear had noticed a stegomyia settling on his hand. Instead of brushing it away, he deliberately allowed it to bite him, mistaking it for a harmless species. This time Lazear *did* come down with yellow jack. He developed a chill on September 19. His eyes became bloodshot, his face red. On the third day came the familiar yellowing of the skin. On September 25, Jesse Lazear was dead, a martyr to medicine.

It was a costly way of proving that the mosquito really did transmit yellow fever. "Now it is my turn to take the bite," Reed declared, but General Wood ordered him not to. His life was too important. There were others who could be risked instead.

Now the Army built an isolation ward for Reed, a mile from the base. It was named Camp Lazear. There, Reed would experiment under carefully controlled conditions until he had proved beyond all doubt that the stegomyia was the disease-carrier.

"I need volunteers who will let themselves be bitten by these mosquitoes," Reed announced. "I'll offer $250 to anyone who'll allow himself to become an experimental subject."

Two men stepped forward. One was Private John R. Kissinger of the Hospital Corps. The other was just a plain civilian citizen, John J. Moran, a headquarters clerk. They volunteered—on the condition that they receive no money. They were offering themselves solely in the interest of humanity, in the name of science.

"Gentlemen, I salute you," Walter Reed told them.

They were cooped up in Camp Lazear. For weeks they lived in airtight isolation, so that there was no chance of accidental infection with yellow fever. Outside, the epidemic raged, and eighty-five victims out of a hundred died. Finally, in December, Kissinger and Moran were exposed to mosquitoes who had previously bitten yellow fever victims. Both men got the disease. Both men recovered.

More volunteers were needed. Reed found five Spaniards who had just come to Cuba as immigrants. He paid them $200 apiece to become guinea pigs for him. Four of the five developed yellow fever. None died.

Now the proof was mounting. The careful experimentation was yielding repeated results. It seemed beyond doubt that the stegomyia did transmit the disease. Reed, though, was not satisfied. He wanted to test the old theories which held that yellow fever was transmitted through contact with the clothes and bedding of fever victims.

New cabins were built at Camp Lazear. Three more volunteers appeared: a doctor named Cooke, and two soldiers named Folke and

Jernegan. They sealed themselves into those mosquito-proof boxes, dressed themselves in the dirty clothes of dead men, lay down on sheets soiled by the discharges of the dying. "You must see that the yellow fever poison is well spread around that room!" Walter Reed instructed.

For weeks the experiment went on, and more and more volunteers joined it. The men exposed themselves to every kind of contact. They slept on pillows soiled with the vomit of yellow fever victims. They slept in the pajamas of the dead!

But no mosquitoes could enter the cabin. And none of the volunteers got yellow fever. The dramatic proof was unquestionable. Mosquitoes, not contact, carried the disease.

Reed wrote, "The essential factor in the infection of a building with yellow fever is the presence therein of mosquitoes that have bitten cases of yellow fever."

And he wrote to his wife, "The prayer that has been mine for twenty years, that I might be permitted in some way or at some time to do something to alleviate human suffering has been granted!"

But he was careful not to take the credit for the initial theory. "It was Finlay's theory," he insisted, "and he deserves great credit for having suggested it, but as he did nothing to prove it, it was rejected by all. . . . Now we have put it beyond cavil."

The villain was identified. Now to wipe him out!

The man for the job was a medical officer, Major William C. Gorgas. Gorgas himself had had yellow fever in 1882, and so was immune. Now he threw himself wholeheartedly into the war against the stegomyia.

Gorgas and his teams roared through Cuba. The way to root out the mosquitoes was to drain the swamps, pour a coating of oil over stagnant water to kill the hatching grubs. Soon there was not a stegomyia to be seen in all Havana. And for the first time in two centuries, there was not a single case of yellow jack in the whole city!

Major Gorgas became *Colonel* Gorgas. In 1904, he went on to Panama, where yellow fever was still a problem, and stamped out the mosquitoes there. Gorgas' work in Panama made possible the building of the Panama Canal, which had been hampered and interrupted by repeated epidemics of yellow jack.

Of course, it was not possible to obliterate every mosquito everywhere. There were always a few lurking about. Until it was known how to deal directly with yellow fever as a disease, the fear of epidemic would not abate. The last epidemic in the U.S. took place in 1905, in Louisiana. But in other parts of the world, where mosquito control was not so well organized, yellow fever still flourished, in Africa and Asia, on the islands of the Pacific, in Brazil.

Other doctors sought ways of defeating the disease itself. The billionaire John D. Rockefeller and his son founded the Rockefeller Institute for medical research, and yellow fever became a major concern of the Institute. A Rockefeller Institute researcher named Adrian Stokes went to Africa to study yellow fever, but contracted the disease himself, and died of it. But Stokes, before he died, made a valuable discovery: Certain species of monkeys were vulnerable to yellow fever. For the first time, experimental animals became available, and it was no longer necessary to repeat the grim risks of Carroll and Lazear.

A colleague of Stokes, Japanese-born Hideyo Noguchi, took up the struggle. Noguchi, too, went to Africa, and found the cause of yellow fever: a virus, unbelievably tiny. He was at work on a vaccine against the virus when he, too, became a martyr to research, dying of yellow fever in 1928. Other Rockefeller Institute doctors continued the work. They found that not one but fourteen species of mosquitoes could transmit the disease, and that many jungle animals were susceptible to it. Mosquitoes picked up the virus by biting a yellow fever victim, and transmitted it by dropping it off in the blood stream of the next person they bit.

Finally a serum was developed, *Virus 17-D*. From 1939 on, many millions of people have been vaccinated against yellow fever, and today it is almost unknown throughout the world, an item of medical history rather than a terrifying plague.

And what of Walter Reed? Why did he not take part in the search for the yellow fever virus?

Walter Reed was dead. He died at the height of his fame, in November, 1902, at the age of 51. It was not yellow fever that carried him off, either. It was acute appendicitis. He died at the Army General Hospital, in Washington, D.C.

"I leave so little," Reed said just before his death.

He meant that he had left little money for his wife and daughter. Congress voted his widow a pension of $1,500 a year, handsome enough in those days, though small reward for Walter Reed's services to humanity. Jesse Lazear's widow was also awarded a pension, and later, so was the widow of James Carroll. As for Private Kissinger, he was given $115, and a gold watch, as his reward for volunteering to contract yellow fever.

"I leave so little."

In money, yes. But Walter Reed's legacy to humanity was a great one, and he will be remembered for it long after the great army hospital that bears his name has crumbled into dust. He showed the way with bravery and perseverance, and his accomplishment was great. Not only did he strike a mighty blow against one particular disease, but he set an example of selflessness and courage that must have been an inspiration to the martyrs Stokes and Noguchi and to every other doctor who has since risked his life to solve the riddles of sickness.

"I leave so little."

No, Walter Reed. You left a great deal.

12

Halsted: Doctor, Teacher, Drug Addict

THE GREAT American surgeon of the latter part of the nineteenth century was William Stewart Halsted of Baltimore. No one could match him in surgical technique. He was infinitely careful, monumentally precise. Another surgeon might be satisfied simply to have his patients survive; Halsted was so much of a perfectionist that he worked hard to conceal even the scars of surgery on his patients.

A great surgeon, yes. But a very strange man.

His fussiness about clothing was only part of his eccentricity. He had to have the finest of clothes, the softest of linens. And they had to be spotlessly clean. He would wear expensive suits only two or three times. Because no local laundry could wash his shirts properly, he sent them off to a laundry in Paris. He changed clothes several times a day.

He had other quirks. He rarely smiled. He had many acquaintances, but no friends. He kept the world at arm's length. He was a gourmet, as fanatical about food as he was about laundry service. He often offended his patients with his sarcastic remarks, though he served them well when they came under his knife.

Most people who met William Stewart Halsted simply thought he was peculiar. Only a select few knew that this odd, fussy little man, who selected the beans for his coffee one by one, was something other than a crank—that he was, in reality, a living martyr to scientific research, a man who had experimented on himself and who had paid a steep price for his courage.

Halsted was one of four men who gave vigor and impetus to American medicine at the end of the last century. The other three were William Welch, the pathologist; Howard Atwood Kelly, the gynecologist; and William Osler, the physician. These three and Halsted were the first teachers at Johns Hopkins Medical School in Baltimore.

The thing that they taught was something every doctor in each generation must learn anew: that medical understanding springs from observation, experience, research. Books and lectures are important, of course, but a true doctor has to see with his own eyes, feel with his own hands. He cannot rely on established authority, on dogmas handed down from the past.

We have seen over and over again how the dead hand of dogma choked medicine—in ancient India, in Egypt, in Rome, in Galen-dominated medieval Europe. Osler, Kelly, Welch, and Halsted kept American medicine from the same fate.

Halsted was born in 1852, to a wealthy New York family with a house on Fifth Avenue and a country home as well. He had a fine private education, and then, as a wealthy boy should, he went on to Phillips Academy at Andover, and then to Yale.

As a boy he spent long summer hours dissecting toads and newts in his parents' garden. (I wonder how many millions of unhappy amphibians have been sacrificed to feed the curiosities of boys like Halsted, Vesalius, and John Hunter!) But young Halsted did not show any real interest in science. In his college days he was more interested in the latest men's fashions, and in sports. In 1873 he was elected captain of Yale's football team. Perhaps he thought he had attained the absolute peak of fame!

He was good-looking, cheerful, full of pranks in those days. He could be witty when he wanted to be, but his wit had a cutting edge sometimes, and he made not a few enemies with a casually demolishing bit of sarcasm. At the age of 21 he seemed like many another Ivy League college boy of his day—no scholar, but well equipped for enjoying good food, good clothes, and high living. No particular career seemed in store for him.

Then, when he was a senior at Yale, he happened to buy a copy of a famous medical text that is still in use today, Gray's *Anatomy*. No one knows what chance whim led him to purchase the bulky volume. But it transformed his life.

Leafing through it, Halsted was fascinated by the complexity of the human body, by the miraculous network of veins and arteries, by the elaborate underpinnings of muscle and tendon and bone. A passion for medicine seized him. He wangled his way into the Medical School building to observe operations. By the time he graduated from Yale, he knew his ambition: to be a surgeon.

Overnight his lighthearted playboy ways dropped from him. He enrolled at Columbia University's College of Physicians and Surgeons, then as now a great medical school and no place for a playboy. After two years at P. & S. Halsted grew impatient, though, and applied to Bellevue Hospital for the post of interne. Today, it is necessary to complete four years at medical school and receive a degree, in order to become an interne. But the rules were easier in those days. A year or two of formal training was enough to get onto a hospital staff.

Halsted passed the examination. In 1876, he went to Bellevue as an interne.

Bellevue was anything but a progressive hospital in those years. Only two doctors on its entire staff followed the teachings of Lister. The rest still clung to the old ways. "Wash my hands before surgery? Don't be ridiculous!" they snorted, and off they went to operate with dirty scalpels, wearing blood-stained butcher's frocks. Lister? Antisepsis? "Nonsense! Nothing but sheer twaddle!"

So the youthful Halsted was treated to all the hideous sights of the old school of surgery. He saw the festering wounds, the deaths from shock, the bungled administration of anesthetics, and all the rest.

The standard treatment for a compound fracture was still amputation at that hospital. The place was full of recuperating amputees, naturally. They were all kept in the same ward, and a grim place it was. The stumps had a way of bursting open every few days, blood spurting out wildly.

The internes could not keep up with all the cases of hemorrhage, so a grisly method of checking on the patients was devised: the amputees were arranged in a semicircle, with their stumps pointing inward toward some hapless interne. He sat there on a stool in the center of the group, ready to leap into action in case any stump began to hemorrhage.

Halsted, like any sensitive young man, was shocked by the nightmares hidden under Bellevue's roof. It was all the more dismaying to him because he knew something of Lister's work, and understood that most of these amputations and deaths had been needless. But he could not question the policies of his superiors. He weathered the Bellevue chamber of horrors, and in 1877 was granted his M.D.

He moved on to New York Hospital and began his surgical career. At the same time he studied pathology under his friend, William Welch, who was giving private courses in an old morgue building. After a year, Halsted decided he simply did not know enough about medicine, and he went off to Europe for two years of study in Germany and Austria.

It was an eye-opening trip. He viewed the most modern hospitals of Europe, saw Lister's antiseptic techniques in practice, and was startled by the differences between the Austrian clinics and those of New York. He wrote:

> I was impressed with the fact that our surgeons were greatly handicapped in most of their operations by lack of proper instruments, particularly of artery clamps. . . . Rarely had I seen in our country, prior to my first visit to Europe, more than one artery clamp at a time left hanging in a wound. Clamps were too few for this—four to three or even two being considered

ample for an operation. Few hospitals, in New York at least, pos-
sessed as many as six artery clamps in 1880.

I recall vividly an operation in Vienna, performed by Mikulicz
in Billroth's clinic in 1879. Americans, newly arrived in Austria,
were greatly amused at seeing perhaps a dozen clamps left hang-
ing in a wound of the neck while the operator proceeded with
his dissection, and were inclined to ridicule the method as untidy
or uncouth. Slowly it dawned upon us that we in America were
novices in the art as well as the science of surgery.

Halsted returned to New York full of European ideas, and became
an associate surgeon at Roosevelt Hospital. He immediately began
buying clamps, or *hemostats,* by the dozen, and using them to clamp
off arteries during surgery to prevent excess bleeding. At a time when
no one really understood the connection between bleeding and surgical shock, Halsted was almost a fanatic about tying off blood vessels
and reducing bleeding during an operation to an absolute minimum.

He was busy in the next few years. He had a private surgical practice, he taught anatomy at Columbia, and he held surgeon's posts in
half a dozen hospitals at once, while conducting private surgical lessons
at night and even finding time to go on studying pathology with Welch.

He was nearing 30, now. His hair was retreating, he had grown
a little beard, and he was becoming well known as an up-and-coming
young surgeon.

He had tremendous confidence in himself—rightly so. Two inci-
dents from this period show how much faith Halsted had in his own
judgment and ability. In 1881, when his own sister lay near death
from hemorrhaging after childbirth, Halsted boldly injected blood
from his own veins into hers. Since the theory of blood types was unknown then, he had no way of knowing how risky the transfusion was.
But his sister lived. The following year, he performed a gall bladder
operation on his own mother. Several experts warned him not to
attempt it, but Halsted carried the operation off successfully though
he had never before done such an operation on anyone.

Now he turned to a new field of interest: local anesthesia.

Anesthesia was less than 40 years old at that time. It was still a crude affair. The patient was heavily dosed with ether or chloroform, until complete unconsciousness resulted. Ether and chloroform are both powerful drugs, and sometimes a heavy dose could have bad effects on a patient whose system was already weakened by disease.

Halsted dreamed of some local anesthetic with pinpoint effect, that would not be such a drain on the patient's vitality. Why anesthetize the whole body just to operate in one small area, he asked?

He experimented with various local anesthetics. When he felt ready to operate on a human being under local anesthesia, he asked Bellevue for permission to use their facilities.

The medical conservatives who controlled that hospital refused. "There'll be no such operation performed here!" they told him.

Halsted wangled permission to erect a tent on the hospital lawn and perform the operation there. He spent $10,000 of his own money to build the tent, which had an inlaid maple floor and its own plumbing system. The operation was successful.

He was at the height of his young manhood—a hearty, gay man with a wide circle of friends, a love of the arts, fine food, antique rugs. In 1884 he was 32, and scaling new heights in surgery daily. But in that year he learned of the new anesthetic, cocaine.

Cocaine had been under study in Europe for a decade. It was a drug adapted from South American coca leaves. The Indians of South America liked to chew the leaves, claiming that it relaxed them and made them feel "stronger."

The German and Austrian doctors working with cocaine had found that it was an excellent local anesthetic. It could be injected into the tissues around a nerve and it would provide complete freedom from pain in a highly limited area.

And cocaine had another interesting property. The doctors working with it found that by sniffing small quantities, they could heighten their own mental powers. Their bodies needed less sleep, and their minds became almost superhumanly keen. They could do brilliant work for hours, even days on end, without growing tired.

But there were two things about cocaine that no one yet realized. The first was that it provided only a short-lived heightening of mental powers, only in the early stages of taking the drug.

The second thing was that cocaine was habit-forming.

Halsted and two other young doctors plunged into cocaine research —not only experimenting with it as an anesthetic, but sniffing it themselves and enjoying the intensified mental powers it gave. By 1885, Halsted published his first paper on cocaine anesthesia. But it was a fuzzy and illogical paper. The doctors who puzzled their way through its disjointed sentences wondered, "What is happening to Halsted's writing style?"

The trouble was not with Halsted's writing style, but with Halsted's mind. For by this time he was no longer experiencing heightened mental ability. On the contrary, his brain was clouding, his awareness growing dimmer. He had been sniffing the drug regularly. He and the two young doctors who had joined him in the study were drug addicts.

They made an attempt to break the habit. No use. Whenever they deprived themselves of cocaine, their drug-accustomed bodies cried out. Their legs grew wobbly, their digestions went haywire, and— worst of all—their minds suffered. They drifted off into a dreamworld of narcotic fantasies.

Halsted's two friends remained addicts to the day of their death. But Halsted broke the habit. It took a phenomenal effort of will. He withdrew to a mental hospital in Rhode Island and spent a full year in seclusion, forcing himself to defeat his craving for the drug. It was a year of endless torture.

He emerged cured. But he had changed. His old gaiety and gregariousness were gone. So, too, was his sweeping energy, his gusto for life and work. The new Halsted was a timid, fussy, austere person, melancholy and shy. Drug addiction had broken his health and broken his spirit as well.

At first he had difficulty focusing his mind on medicine. The world was still a hazy, uncertain place for him. Gradually he was able to re-build his shattered career, but now and then he would sink back into the shadowy world of drug addiction. It was an endless struggle for him to deny the craving—a struggle that sapped his energy and drained his strength.

But a wonderful new opportunity turned up to save him. His old friend Welch had moved to Baltimore, to prepare for the opening of the new Johns Hopkins Medical School. He invited Halsted to join him. "You'll have a laboratory all your own," Welch promised him.

It was ideal. Halsted could do research without having to face other people. He could live the withdrawn life he now preferred. And he would have Welch nearby to watch over him in case the drug tempta-tion became too strong for him again.

Halsted went to Johns Hopkins. It seems that at this time he was still taking cocaine in small quantities—"tapering off," reducing his intake of the drug until he could cease altogether. To restore his health, he took a trip to South America, and something ugly happened on the return voyage. Halsted's supply of cocaine gave out. He suffered the torments of the damned without cocaine, and finally broke into the captain's cabin, where he had heard there was stock of cocaine. Ransacking the place, Halsted stole the cocaine. It was the most degrading incident of his life and did not become known until after his death.

That was the low point for Halsted. When he returned, he went back to the hospital in Rhode Island for a brief stay and afterward had no problems with cocaine again. There are those who suspect that he remained a mild cocaine addict all his life, but, if he did, there is no hint of it in the quality of his professional work.

During the next two years he studied many medical problems: stitching the intestines after surgery; the functions of the thyroid gland; the structure of blood clots; the techniques of closing operative incisions. He experimented on dogs and came to many far-reaching conclusions about how to avoid hemorrhage and shock in surgery.

By 1889 his mind was clear again. He was able to reenter medical practice. But, though he quickly demonstrated that he was as skillful a surgeon as he had ever been, his private life was a strange one. He lived the life of a hermit, hurrying home after his hours at the laboratory and rarely going out. Since hardly anyone but a few close associates knew of his drug problem, he was thought to be simply peculiar. He saw no one socially, said little, always seemed lost in his own dark moods.

In his professional life all went well. In 1889 he became associate professor of surgery at Johns Hopkins, and in 1892 he became chief surgeon and professor of surgery, one of the "Great Four" of Johns Hopkins.

And then Halsted married. It seems like a strange decision for a man of his moody, withdrawn ways. But he found a wife who seemed to match him in many respects. She was Caroline Hampton, whose family had been aristocrats in the South until they were ruined by the Civil War. Caroline was the head nurse in Halsted's operating room. Aloof and distant herself, ladylike and formal, her quiet dignity was appealing to the coldly reserved Halsted, and the doctor took her to wife.

Before she retired from nursing, Caroline was indirectly responsible for one great advance in hospital practice. She came to Halsted one day in 1890 or 1891, complaining that the antiseptic solution used in the operating room was hurting her hands. It was strong stuff, mercuric chloride, and Caroline's skin was fair and delicate.

"I have an idea," Halsted told her. He had plaster casts of her hands made and sent them off to the Goodyear Rubber Company in New York. Back came a pair of rubber gloves—the first ever to be used in a hospital. They were thick and awkward, but they protected Caroline's hands and could be boiled to make them aseptic. Soon many of Halsted's nurses and assistants were wearing them.

Of course, the surgeon himself needed the full freedom of his fingers.

Caroline's gloves were not for him. But Halsted saw the advantages of some kind of glove, and in 1896 he went back to Goodyear, this time with *bronze* casts of his own hands. They supplied him with thin, flexible, tight-fitting gloves. The day of the bare-handed surgeon was over.

As a surgeon, Halsted's style was precise and meticulous. He regarded the old, slashing, speed-record school of surgery with contempt.

"There is no reason to rush an operation," he declared. After all, proper anesthetic technique would spare the patient from pain. Careful tying-off of blood vessels would prevent loss of blood. Painstaking asepsis would forestall infection. Careful and delicate handling of the patient's tissues would reduce the chance of post-operative shock. Why rush, then? Why imitate the speed-demon methods of the Dark Ages of surgery?

Halsted's operations seemed almost endless to his colleagues. The removal of a breast—an operation usually accompanied by profuse bleeding, and in Halsted's day generally performed in about an hour —took Halsted as long as 4½ hours. Lesser operations that other men did in a matter of minutes took up to an hour for Halsted. He worked fastidiously, precisely matching each layer of muscle and skin, each wrinkle, as he closed the wound. Nor did he ever begin an operation without long preliminary laboratory experimentation on animals. As a result, Halsted's patients scarcely ever went into shock.

This precision of technique was Halsted's greatest contribution to medicine. In his particular specialties—operations for hernia (rupture), breast cancer, and thyroid gland ailments—he revolutionized the standard techniques, and many of Halsted's methods are still in use today.

The operation with which Halsted is most closely connected is that of the removal of the breast for cancer. This was and is a major operation, and cannot be undertaken until it is known whether the patient really had a dangerous cancer or simply a harmless tumor. A tumor can be removed at almost any time, but cancer spreads through the body and must be checked as soon as it is discovered.

The best way of telling how serious a growth is, is to remove tissue from the growth and study it under the microscope. This technique is known as *biopsy*. Biopsy was first introduced in 1879 by a German doctor, Carl Ruge. Kelly, Halsted's colleague at Johns Hopkins, brought the technique to America. It became standard practice at Johns Hopkins to cut a small segment from any growth and examine it before operating.

There was one danger: that by cutting into a malignant growth, the surgeon might stimulate the cancer to expand suddenly and wildly.

"We must be ready to operate immediately after the biopsy," Halsted warned. Waiting two or three days to get the report from the pathologist might be fatal.

So another member of Johns Hopkins' amazing group of medical greats, T. S. Cullen, developed in 1895 the *frozen section* method of biopsy. In this technique, the tumor extract was immediately frozen with carbon dioxide. The pathologist could then quickly stain it and examine it microscopically, and provide a report in a matter of minutes, so that the waiting surgeon could proceed with the removal if the growth turned out to be malignant.

Halsted's second career—his post-addiction career—was an extraordinary one. Personally a withdrawn, unhappy man, by choice almost friendless and virtually a stranger even to his own wife, he achieved phenomenal things in the operating room.

He thought of himself as a "conservative" surgeon. By that he did not mean conservative in the sense of blindly reaching for the past—the sort of conservatives who blocked the careers of Vesalius, McDowell, Jenner, Hunter, and so many others—but conservative in the sense of being cautious, maturely critical. Halsted was never fettered by the teachings of the past. His methods were brand new. He made himself known for his dogged insistence on complete hemostasis (control of bleeding), absolute asepsis, precision of work, gentleness in handling tissues.

He was a strange, lonely, tormented man. He was as much of a martyr to medicine as Jesse Lazear. Lazear, dead of a mosquito's bite, gave his life at 34. Halsted lived till 1922, when he was 70. But the shadow of his drug addiction was never far from him, and he had become an addict while searching for better ways to free men from pain.

For this we respect him. He was not only a tragic figure but a great doctor—the founder of modern conservative surgery.

13

Cushing: Of Brains and Books

Brain SURGERY is thousands of years old. Prehistoric man practiced trepanning in cave days, and trepanning never went out of fashion. It was performed when a skull had been fractured and there was bone pressure on the brain. It was performed in the Middle Ages for epilepsy, "to let the devil out." It was even performed for headaches. The death rate was always fearsome.

The main anatomical problem was that no one had much of an idea how the brain functioned. Brain surgery was conducted on a hit-or-miss basis. In cases of brain abscess, the surgeon simply drilled holes all over the skull until a spurt of pus told him he had hit the abscess. The inner convolutions of the brain were as mysterious to the medical man as the far side of the Moon was to the astronomer.

Some of the mystery began to clear in 1861, when Paul Broca demonstrated that certain specific areas of the brain controlled the functions of specific parts of the body. Other researchers extended and refined Broca's ideas.

The first important brain surgeon was Sir William Macewen. In 1879 Sir William, professor of surgery at Glasgow, successfully removed a tumor in the *dura mater,* or membrane that covers the brain. Later, he developed a technique for operating on blood clots pressing on the brain, and for removing abscesses, pus formations. By 1893, he could claim 18 successes in 19 cases of brain abscess, where once the death rate had been a flat 100 percent.

Other surgeons cautiously followed Macewen's lead. During the 1880's and 1890's, a number of brain operations were performed, and, though many of the patients died, there was hope for developing a safe method of operating on the brain.

The early surgical technique was not exactly delicate. Choosing the area for entering the skull was still done largely by guesswork. The patient, his scalp shaved, would be chloroformed, and then the surgeon would study the skull, eventually choosing a site and marking it —sometimes by hammering in a tack.

A tourniquet would be tied around the scalp, for it bleeds copiously. Then the surgeon would set to work. The European technique used a hammer and chisel, but American surgeons preferred the trephine, an instrument that cut a round hole and removed a "button" of bone. This button was kept to one side during the operation in an antiseptic solution, and was generally replaced afterward, in the hope that it would grow back into place. Sometimes it actually did.

One of the most celebrated brain operations of the day was performed in 1887 by Dr. William Williams Keen of Philadelphia. In this, the first brain tumor operation performed in the United States, Keen was lucky enough to find the site of the tumor on the first try. He used a trephine to make a hole 1½ inches in diameter. This proved to be too small to remove the tumor. With bone clippers, Keen widened the opening to three inches by 2½. Then he cut through the *dura mater* and exposed the brain itself.

The tumor lay right at the surface of the brain. Keen slipped his little finger under it. It was firm, and he lifted it out with "as little difficulty as one scoops an egg out of its shell." The patient survived for many years. The celebrated tumor is still preserved at the Jefferson Medical College in Philadelphia.

Keen's success led to other brain tumor operations. Most ended fatally. Shock or hemorrhage carried off 50 percent of the patients. In a third of the cases, the surgeon failed to find the tumor. Infection cut down many. Through 1905, perhaps one brain tumor operation in ten was successful.

All that soon would change. New techniques, new instruments, would transform brain surgery. And the man most chiefly responsible —the man whose name for many years was synonymous with brain surgery—was an American, Harvey Cushing (1869–1939).

Cushing was a disciple of William Halsted. But he was a great doctor in his own right—perhaps the greatest ever born in the United States.

Cushing was Cleveland-born, but his family was of New England stock. He was the youngest of ten children, and the fourth Cushing doctor. His grandfather, his father, and his older brother were all medical men.

He studied nature in boyhood, collected birds' nests and butterflies, and became a good enough baseball player to be able to make the Yale varsity team at shortstop. The *Yale News* said of him, "Cushing is a very good fielder, but often throws wildly and loses his head." He lost his head—and his temper—often enough. He was hotheaded enough to win himself the nickname, "Pepper Pot."

In 1891 Cushing entered Harvard Medical School. He quickly distinguished himself there for his keenness of observation and for his skill at dissecting. Hard-working, conscientious, Cushing spent his spare time in the wards at the Massachusetts General Hospital, getting a firsthand view of human suffering.

But his medical career nearly came to an end before it was fairly begun. One day in 1893 he was assisting in an operation at the hospital. Although today anesthesia is administered by trained specialists, then it was permissible for medical students to wield the ether cup. Cushing, though he had had little instruction in anesthesia, was told to put the patient "under." The surgeon, Dr. Charles Porter, seemed to be in a hurry. Cushing rushed the job of giving the ether. The moment Dr. Porter began the operation, the patient died.

Cushing was horrified, remorse-stricken. He rushed from the hospital and wandered through Boston all day. That evening, he presented himself to Dr. Porter.

"I'm withdrawing from the medical school," Cushing announced. "I'm not fit to be a doctor. I killed that woman today."

"Don't be a fool," Porter told him. "You had nothing to do with it. She would have died anyway. I could see it from the start."

Cushing continued to brood, but he stayed on at Harvard. The experience had been a searing one, but it taught him the lesson of patience. And it had a practical result. Cushing and a friend worked out a system for making a continuous record of a patient's pulse and respiration during operations, so that the surgeon could tell from moment to moment what his patient's condition was. The use of Cushing's chart system became widespread and undoubtedly saved many lives.

In his final year of medical school, Cushing, 26, witnessed his first brain operation—a compound fracture of the skull. The patient lived, though only one of eight skull fracture victims survived then. Cushing noted the "fearful" hemorrhages, and recognized at once that great loss of blood was perhaps the biggest drawback to safe brain surgery.

Leaving the Massachusetts General Hospital, Cushing wangled an appointment to Johns Hopkins as Halsted's assistant. This was no simple matter, as Johns Hopkins had incredibly high standards for admission. The beloved teacher William Osler frequently said that he was lucky to be a professor there, for he never could have qualified as a student.

Halsted was then in the early stages of his recovery from drug addiction. Cushing, not knowing the real reason for Halsted's poor health and strange ways, found him moody and hard to get along with. Cushing and Halsted respected each other as surgeons, but were never very warm friends. (Cushing once wrote to his fiancée, "I was very rude to the Professor [Halsted] yesterday. Sorry, but couldn't help it. Some day I will tell him I don't like him and then pack up my duds and go home.")

In the small medical community around Johns Hopkins, Cushing now and then received the rare privilege of an invitation to Halsted's home. He went to dinner there once and was awed by the delicacy of the food—caviar, roast oysters, terrapin stew, quail in jelly with pâté de foie gras, a soufflé, and rare wines. The Halsteds presided over this feast in aloof majesty. But the following month, when Cushing took his fiancée Kate to meet the Halsteds, the huge Halsted house was without a fire, and Mrs. Halsted came out to meet her guests in a soiled butcher's apron—she had been working with her dogs.

"They are so peculiar, eccentric, so unlike other people yet so interesting doubtless because of their oddities," Cushing wrote his mother, "that one is inclined to shelve his thoughts about them alongside of those of people from fiction—Dickens perhaps."

Halsted's poor health forced him to absent himself from the hospital frequently. The great burden of his work fell on his assistant, Cushing, who was irritated and overstrained from having to do not only his own heavy work but much of Halsted's, too. He recognized, though, that this gave him an opportunity to acquire great surgical experience.

Cushing was troubled and depressed by Halsted's coolness to him. There was one touchy moment in 1898 when Cushing began to do some research into the use of cocaine as a local anesthetic—the very thing that had blighted Halsted's life, though Cushing did not know it! Cushing took his results to Halsted. But the older man was not interested. He shrugged and turned away. Cushing was hurt. "Doesn't he care at all about my research?" Not for many years did he learn why Halsted had so little desire to talk about cocaine.

Unable to break through Halsted's wall of reserve, Cushing turned instead to William Osler. Osler, a warmhearted and popular teacher, served as Cushing's mentor for many years. Osler was a great collector of rare books on medical history, and he passed his enthusiasm along to Cushing, who also formed a superb collection of medical classics. After Osler's death, Cushing wrote a biography of Osler which is probably the finest work by one doctor about another. When it was published, in 1925, it won the Pulitzer Prize.

Though they were never friends, Cushing and Halsted worked well in the operating room. Cushing shared Halsted's love of precision, his meticulous ways. Halsted saw in him a fit inheritor of his own surgical tradition. Cushing was capable of operating for hours at a time, without fatigue, without growing careless. And in the delicacy of his touch he surpassed even Halsted.

Cushing was once Halsted's patient. In September, 1898, Cushing developed appendicitis. It was only ten years since the first successful appendectomies had been performed, and the operation was still highly risky. But Halsted operated, and Cushing came through well.

In 1900 Cushing went to Europe, where he observed the masters of surgery at work. When he returned, his appointment at Johns Hopkins had expired, but he applied for a reappointment. He wanted to specialize in brain surgery—the first doctor ever to do so.

Cushing's brain operations were already winning him acclaim. That year, one of Cushing's Yale classmates had met William Osler, and asked him, "How is my friend Harvey Cushing getting along?" Osler replied, "Your friend Cushing has opened the book of surgery in a new place."

Halsted, though, opposed the idea. He thought brain surgery held no promise. "Look at the hospital records," he told Cushing. 36,000 patients had been admitted to Johns Hopkins between 1889 and 1899. Of these, only 32 had been found to have brain tumors. Only two of those 32 had actually been operated on, and both of those had died of the surgery. What kind of field was that, Halsted asked, for a young man to enter? Halsted suggested that Cushing go into orthopedics instead—the correcting of limb deformities, especially in children. Now, there was a field with promise!

Cushing was stubborn. Little wonder that brain surgery was so risky, he argued, considering that no one bothered to specialize in it! He would be the pioneer. He would show the way.

Halsted, a onetime pioneer himself, had grown too cautious with age. In a well-meant attempt to discourage Cushing from throwing away his career, Halsted tried to block his appointment in neurosurgery, or brain surgery. Osler, though, intervened, and Cushing finally had his way. He was allowed to remain at Johns Hopkins and to specialize in neurosurgery.

Cushing began his new career with work on trigeminal neuralgia. This is a painful affliction of the facial nerves. In 1892, a New York surgeon named Frank Hartley had devised a technique for entering the skull and removing the gesserian ganglion, a section of the trigeminal nerve. This halted the pain of the neuralgia, but the death rate from the operation was one in ten.

Cushing was able to halve this. In Hartley's operation, the surgeon often accidentally tore an important artery while trying to reach the ganglion. Cushing was able to avoid this by removing part of the cheekbone and making his approach at a different angle.

Unfortunately, Cushing's elaborate work in this line was largely wasted. Another American surgeon, Charles Frazier, found a simpler and safer way of operating. It was a long time before Cushing could bring himself to adopt Frazier's method, but he finally did.

Cushing's particular specialty in neurosurgery was the brain tumor. At the start, he lost nearly all of his patients, like every other surgeon working in that field. Cushing was discouraged by the fatalities, but he went on. And gradually the death rate dropped.

A brain tumor is a growth within the skull. Since the skull is not a flexible structure, the tumor as it grows must press severely against the brain. This causes headache, vomiting, and eventually blindness, paralysis, or death.

In those early days, most tumors of the brain could not be located and so could not be removed surgically. The customary procedure instead was to remove a flap of bone, creating a "window" in the skull through which the brain could bulge. This relieved some of the pressure as the tumor grew. But at best it gave the patient a few extra months of life.

Cushing worked out a new technique, known as *palliative decompression,* which involved cutting away the flap of bone from under the muscles of the temple or of the back of the skull. This gave the brain the needed expansion room, but the muscles prevented an ugly bulge from forming. However, Cushing knew that the only true treatment for brain tumor had to be surgical removal of the tumor itself.

By 1910 he could claim 16 successes in 64 brain tumor operations. Unlike Keen and the other early brain surgeons, who had lifted the tumors out with their fingers, Cushing introduced the practice of dissecting the tumors with a piece of gauze. This greatly reduced shock and hemorrhage. Even so, mortality ran high. And in more than 40 of his 64 cases, Cushing had had to perform palliative decompression because he could not remove the entire tumor.

The great enemy was still hemorrhage. Cushing set out to conquer bleeding. The kind of hemostats used elsewhere in the body could not be applied to the brain. Cushing perfected little clips of silver wire which he inserted at bleeding points, gently compressing them and sealing them off. These wires were allowed to remain permanently in place. Where even they could not be used, he employed little stamps of muscle fiber to seal off the hemorrhaging areas. Thus, by 1915, Cushing could publish the results of 130 tumor cases with a mortality rate of 8 percent—at a time when the best surgeons were still losing a third or more of their tumor patients.

Another center of Cushing's interest was the pituitary gland, the so-called master gland that controls all the other glands of the body. Pituitary disorders affect growth, physical maturity, intelligence, and much else. The pituitary is located within the skull, which, before Cushing's time, made it impossible to operate for pituitary disorders.

In 1909 he performed the first operation for acromegaly, a condition of extreme growth caused by pituitary overactivity. (Charles Byrne, the giant that John Hunter caused so much trouble for, had acromegaly.) Cushing made a semicircular incision in the patient's forehead and inserted a sharp spoon. He was able to scoop out half the gland. The patient recovered.

In the three years that followed, Cushing performed a number of operations for pituitary tumors. When he published his important book on the subject in 1912 he could claim a mortality rate of 14 percent. By 1927, however, this figure had been cut to just 4 percent as Cushing's skill grew.

Like many of the great doctors, Cushing had a low boiling point. He worked under great strain and had spells of bad temper, impatience, and depression when not at the operating table. He frequently roasted an assistant or nurse who bungled, sparing no scorn. Even Osler, who rarely criticized anyone, had to speak out about Cushing's habit of criticizing his assistants, warning him in a letter, "This, I need scarcely say would be absolutely fatal to your success here. The arrangement of the Hospital staff is so peculiar that loyalty to each other, even in the minutest particulars, is an essential. I know that you will not mind this from me as I have your interest at heart."

It came as a complete surprise to Cushing that he had been rude to anyone. Anguished, he offered to resign. Osler managed to calm him down. But even afterward, Cushing was never noted for a smooth temper, and he made many enemies—though no one denied his surgical greatness.

His operating style was a crisp, no-nonsense one. He rarely smiled, displayed no geniality as he went about the tense business of opening a human skull. He insisted on absolute silence when he worked. His operations lasted hours at a time, and anyone who dared say a needless word during those long stretches would get an unforgettable tongue-lashing from the surgeon.

Not even Cushing was immune to failure. Once, performing a brain tumor operation, he removed the tumor with his usual skill, and, as he finished the job, noticed what seemed to be the stem of the tumor still in the patient's skull. He took it in his forceps and cut it off. To his horror, he realized that what he had cut was a small artery. Blood spurted. There was no way of dealing with such a happening then. The patient would bleed to death, as everyone around Cushing well realized.

No one dared to speak. The great surgeon put down his instrument, bent over the patient—who was under local anesthesia, and still conscious—and said, "You must not worry now. In a very few minutes you are going to feel better." The patient died as Cushing helplessly watched.

During World War I Cushing went to Europe and operated on battlefield victims, giving up a lucrative practice to do so. He spent several years overseas, frequently clashing with the military authorities. They felt that even Harvey Cushing should obey their orders, but Cushing felt otherwise.

He shared in a tragedy of the war. Revere Osler, the only child of William Osler, was an officer in the British Army. On the night of August 30, 1917, Cushing learned that Revere was seriously wounded. Cushing rushed to the bedside—Revere was one of his closest friends—but nothing could be done. Osler's son died during the night, and it was Cushing's sad duty to pass the news to the aging Osler.

While in service, Cushing was stricken with a strange ailment that left his limbs numb and unsteady. Though he recovered his surgical skills, his legs and feet were never the same again. He operated less frequently after the war and experienced constant pain.

His later life was darkened by a tragedy that paralleled Osler's. Cushing's eldest son Bill was strong-willed and stubborn like his father, and the two had quarreled endlessly. But as Bill grew to manhood, father and son became close friends, and the old quarrels died down. In May, 1924, Bill wrote from college:

> I am just beginning to realize that you have always done the right thing. I only wish you had taken me across your knee and spanked me. I don't know what started me thinking. Perhaps I have come to the turning point. . . .

But two years later, in June, 1926, Bill was killed in an automobile accident. Cushing was scheduled to perform an operation when the news reached him. He closed himself in his study for a while, then went through with the three-hour operation. No one knew until afterward what a blow he had suffered.

Bill's death rocked Cushing deeply. But, unlike Osler, he had other children—a second son, Henry, and three girls, the famous "Cushing girls," Barbara, Betsey, and Mary. Betsey was one day to marry the son of Franklin Delano Roosevelt.

In the year of Bill's death Cushing made an important surgical "first"—he took up the use of electric needles for brain surgery and performed the first cauterization of a brain tumor late in 1926.

In his later years he remained active, despite constant pain. At the age of 62, in 1931, he performed his 2,000th brain tumor operation, recorded by motion picture cameras. The following year, he identified a previously unknown pituitary disease that is known today as Cushing's Disease.

When he was 63, he retired from active practice, but let himself be given the post of professor of neurology at Yale. Like every great doctor, he believed in the value of firsthand experience, and taught this in his classes:

> It would be an admirable thing if every student, before his graduation, be required, under the control and supervision of his teachers or the district physician of the community, to engage in actual house-to-house practice, armed perhaps with nothing more than a clinical thermometer, a stethoscope, his fingers, and wits, supplemented perhaps by a microscope and a few simple dyes. . . .

He turned to writing and to the collecting of books on medical history. His great love was Vesalius, and he surrounded himself with every edition of every book written by or about the King of Anatomists. Cushing's "bio-bibliography" of Vesalius, published after his death, displays his love of books and the depth of his medical knowledge.

At the age of 70, Cushing suffered a heart attack after lifting a heavy folio volume of Vesalius. Three days later he died—but not before he had heard the latest report on the new library building at Yale that would house his collection of books. An autopsy revealed a small tumor in his brain.

Few men have ever dominated one branch of surgery the way Cushing dominated brain surgery. Before Cushing, brain surgery was *terra incognita*—unknown territory. Today, brain operations are as common—and almost as safe—as appendectomies. Harvey Cushing worked a one-man revolution in brain surgery, and his rank among the medical immortals is forever secure.

14

Salk: An End to Polio

For a whole generation growing up today, the word "polio" holds little terror. It it only a word, a name for a disease people used to have, an old, nearly extinct disease like smallpox or yellow fever.

It has not always been this way. When I was going to school, and that was not so very long ago, the President of the United States wore heavy steel braces on his legs, and moved about in a wheelchair. Franklin Delano Roosevelt was a polio victim, the most famous one in the world. Almost everyone knew someone in his neighborhood who had been paralyzed by polio. The newspapers regularly ran stories about people who had to live in *iron lungs*—breathing machines that did the work for the paralyzed chest muscles. In 1952, 3,300 Americans died of polio, and many thousands were permanently paralyzed. Ten years later, there were only a few thousand *cases* of polio in the country, most of them mild, and hardly anyone died of the disease.

The man whose name will forever be associated with the conquest of polio is a shy, publicity-hating doctor who will never again know a moment of real privacy. He is Jonas Salk. His name exploded into fame on April 12, 1955—ten years to the day after the death of polio victim F.D.R.—when headlines round the world blared the news that the Salk Polio Vaccine had passed its final exam, and had been proved effective!

Of course, the story of the fight against polio does not begin with Jonas Salk, nor, as we will see, does it end with him. Salk capped an effort that had been going on for many years. He provided the final blow that toppled polio. But he was not alone.

Polio is an old story. A carved Egyptian slab a thousand years older than Hippocrates shows a boy with one leg wasted and shrunken, a once-familiar sign of infantile paralysis. But it was not until 1784 that a British physician, Dr. Michael Underwood, identified polio as a distinct disease.

Oddly enough, there were no great polio epidemics before the twentieth century. This is because in past centuries sanitation was so poor that human wastes—containing the polio virus—were heaped up everywhere. Most people contracted a mild form of polio in childhood, and were thereafter immune. The older a person is when he is first exposed to polio, the more severe the attack is likely to be. With the coming of modern sanitation, exposure to polio virus was less common, and few people built up immunities. Epidemics could thus sweep entire communities. It sounds like a paradox—greater cleanliness made polio a more dangerous disease!

In 1894 the first polio epidemic in its history struck the United States. Hundreds of children in Vermont came down with a baffling new disease. It began with an upset stomach, a headache, a stiff neck. Fever and convulsions followed—and then, all too often, paralysis or death.

The new disease struck repeatedly. And it was worst, not in primitive parts of the world, but in those countries that were most modern about hygiene—Sweden, England, the United States. An epidemic in New York in 1916 brought the whole giant city to the edge of panic. Polio seemed to prefer to strike children, and the summer was the danger time. The coming of hot weather was a time of fear for every parent.

In 1909, Dr. Karl Landsteiner, the Austrian doctor who is most famous for his identification of the human blood types, proved that polio was an infectious disease. He ground up the spinal cords of children who had died of polio, and gave the preparations to monkeys. They contracted polio. But no one could locate the organism that was responsible.

Later that same year, Dr. Simon Flexner and Dr. Paul A. Lewis of the Rockefeller Institute in New York carried out similar experiments. *The Scientific American* for February, 1910, carried this report:

> In September of 1909 [Flexner and Lewis] inoculated monkeys with emulsions of human spinal cord and later with emulsions of the cords of monkeys that had developed paralysis after injection of the first emulsion. In one series, seven monkeys were each successively inoculated with the virus from the cord or cortex of its predecessor, the disease regularly resulting. Flexner and Lewis have found that the virus of infantile paralysis is of the same nature as that of smallpox. . . . There should be no reason in science why a vaccine or an immunizing agent against poliomyelitis should not in good time be forthcoming.

In 1921, 39-year-old Franklin Delano Roosevelt was struck down by polio. The rising young political leader was paralyzed from the waist down. He struggled back from paralysis, trying anything that might help him rebuild his strength.

Someone suggested that swimming in naturally warm waters at a certain Georgia resort had been beneficial to polio victims. Roosevelt went there in 1924. He found that swimming in the warm waters did indeed strengthen his paralyzed legs. He bought the resort, calling it the Georgia Warm Springs Foundation. Polio victims from all over the country went there for treatment. If they could not pay, they were accepted anyway. Roosevelt and some of his friends solicited donations from rich people to support the work of the Foundation.

In 1932, Roosevelt was elected President. As a public official, he could no longer operate a private sanatorium. Other citizens took over the job of raising money for the Foundation. The fact that the President himself was a polio victim gave fresh public interest to the fight against this disease. An annual campaign called The March of Dimes began on President Roosevelt's birthday, January 30, 1934. Four years later, this fund grew into the National Foundation for Infantile Paralysis, whose purpose was to sponsor scientific research into the causes of polio.

It was known that polio was caused by a virus. Viruses are strange, fantastically small organisms that inhabit a borderline world between life and nonlife. A Russian scientist named Ivanovsky discovered them late in the nineteenth century. He could not actually see them— a million viruses lined up would not cover a single inch—but he deduced their existence from experimental evidence. Today, powerful electron microscopes can spy into the world of the virus.

A bacterial microbe is a living creature that reproduces under any favorable conditions. But viruses are different. They can only reproduce when they enter a living cell. Like little generals, they take over the cell and force it to produce many duplicates of the virus. This process usually kills or damages the cell, and the new army of viruses bursts forth, going out to find new cells in which to reproduce.

The polio virus attacks nerve cells. It has a particular fondness for the cells of the spinal cord and brain. As each virus carries on its attack against an individual cell, the entire nervous system is weakened.

The hope of the National Foundation for Infantile Paralysis—and of everyone else—was that a vaccine could be developed that would give the body the power to resist the attack of the polio virus. It was known that once a person had had polio, even a mild, nonparalytic form, he was usually able to resist the disease even during time of epidemic. If there were only some safe way of giving everyone a mild case of polio, and thus building up an immunity.

But there were so many problems.

Problem number one was that scientists did not have a ready supply of polio virus for experimental use. Before 1949, there was only one way to grow polio virus: by inoculating a monkey with the virus, and waiting till the monkey contracted polio. Then the animal could be killed and his spinal cord, containing virus, removed.

But monkeys were expensive, and the method was slow. And it was impossible to use virus grown in this way to make polio vaccine, anyway. Such a vaccine would be contaminated with the nervous tissue of monkeys, and this could cause an allergic reaction in humans who received the vaccine. An inflammation of the brain more deadly than polio itself could result.

This problem was conquered by three Harvard scientists—Dr. John F. Enders, Dr. Thomas Weller, and Dr. Frederick Robbins. They found a way to grow polio virus in a test tube. The virus would thrive on many kinds of tissue, but it preferred monkey's kidney tissue. The danger of contamination from nervous tissue was eliminated, and for the first time researchers had a plentiful supply of polio vaccine.

The second problem was to find out how polio virus got into the nerve cells of the brain or spinal cord. Some scientists felt that the virus traveled through the nerves only. If this were true, there was no further point in trying to perfect a polio vaccine. For a vaccine would have to circulate through the blood stream. If the polio virus moved through the nerves, vaccine and virus would never clash. Some doctors felt quite strongly that the virus entered the brain and spinal cord by way of the nerve endings in the nose, and this meant no vaccine could help.

The answer came in 1952. Dr. Dorothy Horstmann of Yale and Dr. David Bodian of Johns Hopkins demonstrated the true route of the polio virus. They showed how it first enters the digestive tract, and then passes into the bloodstream. It travels through the blood to its ultimate goal, the brain.

It was an important step. Now, at last, there was reason to believe a vaccine would be useful. A vaccine would create *antibodies*—defensive cells that would live in the blood. When the polio virus entered the bloodstream, the antibodies would swoop into action and intercept the virus before it could reach the vital nerve cells. This was how immunity worked in the bodies of those who had had a mild case of polio. They already had the polio antibodies in their blood. But was there some way of creating the antibodies artificially, without causing polio?

One big obstacle remained. There were over 100 different types of polio virus. Some were deadly, others were not. They had to be studied and classified. A vaccine could not be developed until it was known which specific viruses had to be singled out for attack.

The National Foundation for Infantile Paralysis provided funds so that research teams could sort through these hundred-odd polio viruses to find the deadly ones. One of these research teams was set up at the University of Pittsburgh. And here is where the name of Jonas Salk enters the story. He was in charge of the group at Pittsburgh.

Jonas Salk was born in New York City in 1914, and he was two years old when that city was terrorized by the great polio epidemic of 1916. His father was a manufacturer of women's clothes, none too successful. Jonas took part-time jobs to help pay for his education.

He attended Townsend Harris High School—a special school for unusual students, no longer in operation. At Townsend Harris, the high school course lasted three years instead of four, though the work was far more advanced than the normal high school curriculum. Young Salk showed no particular interest in science there.

He went on to the College of the City of New York. He planned to become a lawyer, but, "just out of curiosity," he took a few science courses. They fascinated him. When he graduated from college, at 19, he announced that he was giving up his law ambitions and intended to study medicine. But not to become a rich doctor with a large practice. He had no intention of practicing medicine at all. He planned to remain in the laboratory, doing medical research.

The decision bewildered his friends and family. "There's no money in research!" they told him.

Jonas Salk shrugged. Money had never been of great interest to him, anyway. And now scientific research was.

He enrolled in New York University Medical School and won a

fellowship to do protein research. In his final year, he began to study viruses, working with the famed virus specialist, Dr. Thomas Francis, Jr. Salk received his M.D. in 1939, did his interning at a New York hospital, and then received another fellowship that enabled him to go into virus research.

He settled down at the University of Michigan's School of Public Health. His old medical school professor, Dr. Francis, was now in charge there. They worked together on viruses—not the polio virus, though, but that of influenza.

In 1947 Salk was offered a glittering opportunity. The University of Pittsburgh, sensing his great promise, invited him to come and head a new department, the Department of Virology—virus study. Salk accepted. He moved back east, and for the next few years devoted himself to influenza virus research in Pittsburgh. Then came the grant from the National Foundation to do polio virus typing.

By this time—1951—other researchers had made great strides in classifying the hundred polio viruses. They had already found that the hundred viruses could be grouped in three main categories. Someone who had polio caused by a Type I virus would be immune to any further invasions of Type I virus—but he might still be struck down by Type II or Type III!

That explained one earlier mystery. In 1935, a pioneering polio vaccine had been developed, but it failed woefully, even causing death in some of those who were vaccinated. Now it was seen that the early vaccine had guarded against only one of the three types. A true polio vaccine would have to protect against all kinds of polio virus.

Over a three-year period, that cost more than a million dollars and the lives of 30,000 monkeys, Dr. Salk studied the hundred polio viruses. He was something of a Johnny-come-lately to polio research, but that was an advantage; he was not weighed down with the accumulated mistakes of the years before. He took a fresh new look at the whole problem.

He began to work on a vaccine that would guard against the three types of polio virus. The vaccine would contain actual polio virus, of all three types. But the virus would be "killed" in formaldehyde, so that it no longer had the power to infect or multiply. Even the killed virus, though, could still stimulate the production of antibodies.

Developing the vaccine was a taxing job, often requiring round-the-clock work. Dr. Salk and his gifted staff of assistants began to grow the three strains of polio virus. After experimenting with a variety of substances on which to nurture the virus, the Salk group chose what they called "Mixture 199," consisting of 62 nutrient ingredients added to the minced kidney tissue of rhesus monkeys. Each flask contained a different strain of polio virus. The viruses were carefully tested, to make sure they had not become contaminated with bacteria or other viruses.

Finally, each pure lot of the polio virus strains was killed in formaldehyde. The three strains of killed virus were mixed to form a vaccine that, Dr. Salk hoped, would give protection against all kinds of polio.

It was a tedious process. If the vaccine were too weak, it would not stimulate the production of antibodies and so would have no benefit. If it were too strong, it might be harmful. Salk experimented on monkeys at first. The blood of the animals was checked for antibody formation. The monkeys were watched for signs of disease.

So far, so good. But monkeys, though they are similar to human beings in many biological respects, are not human. A vaccine that worked on monkeys did not necessarily hold any benefits for men.

There had to be human guinea pigs.

Late in 1952, Dr. Salk tensely prepared to take the giant step. The vaccine would have to be tried on humans. He began carefully, by giving the vaccine to persons who had had polio and had recovered from it. They already had polio antibodies in their blood. But, Dr. Salk reasoned, his vaccine should raise the antibody level, the *titer,* in such people.

The injections were given. It was found that the antibody level did increase. Salk called this a "booster effect."

He was ready now to try the vaccine on children who had never had polio. Early in 1953, he sought out volunteers in Pittsburgh, and injected the vaccine. His own sons were among this first trial group. He injected, and he waited. There were no ill effects. A thousand subjects had been vaccinated, and no one had reacted badly—no fever, no sore arms, and certainly no cases of polio!

Everything looked hopeful. But a thousand subjects was not really very many. Definitive proof was needed.

One way of obtaining this proof was to take the group of vaccinated subjects and deliberately expose them to live polio virus. If they fought off the invasion, the worth of the vaccine would be proven. If not—

No. It is impossible to experiment with human lives in that way. Salk had to find some other means of proof.

The best alternative was a mass experiment. If thousands of children were given the vaccine, and other thousands were *not* given it, and both groups were studied during a polio season, and if the vaccinated group showed a greater resistance to polio than the non-vaccinated group—well, that would prove something!

Salk went to the National Foundation for Infantile Paralysis. He showed them the records of his 1,000 vaccinations. He spoke of his plans for a mass field test.

There was opposition. "A thousand cases aren't enough to go by," some doctors said. "It isn't safe to inject this stuff wholesale!"

Another doctor had a different kind of objection. He was Dr. Albert Sabin of Cincinnati, who was working on his own kind of polio vaccine. Where Salk used killed virus, Sabin was using live but weakened virus. The Salk vaccine, Dr. Sabin said, would provide immunity only for a short period, no more than a year. His own vaccine, which was a long way from the testing stage, would confer more long-lasting protection. Dr. Sabin feared that general acceptance of the Salk vaccine would hinder the development of his own vaccine, which he considered a better one.

While the controversy raged, Dr. Salk went on vaccinating. By early

1954, he had vaccinated some 7,000 children and adults. Some of these had had three shots, others two, some only one. Were they protected against polio?

The summer was coming. The polio season approached. Many thousands of children could be expected to get polio that year, as in every year.

In the spring of 1954, permission came for a mass test of the Salk vaccine. The man chosen to conduct the tests was Dr. Salk's old friend and teacher, Dr. Thomas Francis, Jr. Five large drug companies began to produce the vaccine. Dr. Francis and his co-workers at the University of Michigan prepared to go into action. Starting in April, 1954, the vaccine would be given to millions of school children in the first three grades.

Of the 1,830,000 children who took part in the test, 440,000 were given the cherry-colored Salk vaccine, many getting three shots, and 210,000 were injected with something that *looked* like vaccine, but which actually was a dummy shot of no medical value. Such a dummy shot is called a "placebo." Its purpose is to check on any psychological effect of being vaccinated.

The remaining 1,180,000 children in the test were given no injection at all. All three groups were carefully coded, so the testers would know who had received the vaccine, who had been given the placebo, who had been given nothing.

The months passed. Results on these millions of children streamed into Dr. Francis' laboratory. Electronic computing machines sorted out the data. It took nearly a year to assemble the facts.

Then, on the 10th anniversary of F.D.R.'s death, the results of the test were announced. Dramatically, Dr. Francis read his report before a large audience of tense doctors and eager newsmen.

In the unvaccinated group, 750 had contracted polio.

In the vaccinated group, there were only 113 polio cases.

In the unvaccinated group, there had been 15 polio deaths.

In the vaccinated group, there had been *no* deaths.

Furthermore, no one who had been given the vaccination had developed polio or any other ill effect as a result of being vaccinated. The Salk vaccine worked! And it was safe to use!

Of course, it was not perfect. In the tremendous excitement over the vaccine, the public overlooked the fact that it did not give total protection. Against Type I polio virus, the most dangerous kind, it was only 65 percent effective. Against Types II and III, though, it was 90 to 100 percent effective.

No matter. Nothing is perfect. In one stroke the polio monster had been wounded unto death. Praise for Dr. Salk echoed round the world. Winnipeg, Canada, sent him a 208-foot-long telegram of congratulations. Shopkeepers posted signs reading, "Thank you, Dr. Salk!" There was talk of a Congressional Medal of Honor for Salk, a Nobel Prize.

Honors aplenty came to him. But Salk remained calm and unchanged by fame. Whatever money he received, he turned over to funds for medical research. When a movie producer decided to make a film called *The Triumph of Dr. Salk,* and a reporter asked Salk if he would star in it, he replied, "I have a laboratory. Do I go on working or do I become a movie star?" When another reporter wanted to know if he owned the patent on the vaccine, Salk answered, "The people own the patent. . . . Could you patent the sun?"

He even tried to persuade people to stop calling it the "Salk" vaccine. He insisted, "This is *not* the Salk vaccine. This is a polio vaccine that has come about because of the contributions of many men and women working in many fields. . . ."

Avoiding fame is no easy matter, as Edward Jenner had learned a hundred and fifty years before. But Jonas Salk was eager to get back to his laboratory. Although his vaccine had been found safe and useful, and had been licensed for general public use, it was by no means the ultimate polio weapon. He wanted to refine and perfect it. And other virus-caused diseases awaited study.

And, before the applause for Salk had begun to die down, tragic news came. Two weeks after the vaccine had been put on the market, 11 children who had just received Salk shots came down with polio!

Soon there were 200 new polio victims, and 11 deaths, all attributed to the vaccine.

More than four million doses of polio vaccine had been produced. Millions of children had been vaccinated. It was a moment of terror. A quick check was begun. All the polio vaccine in existence was put on the shelf while the investigators worked.

Finally it was found that a single drug company had manufactured all the Salk vaccine that had caused polio. Through some terrible mistake, sediment containing live virus particles had slipped into several batches of vaccine.

Rigid new testing procedures were instituted. The factors that had allowed such a thing to happen were eliminated—permanently. After that one grim incident, all Salk vaccine that has been manufactured has been perfectly safe.

And, as the years passed and more and more people, young and old, received the Salk shots, the polio statistics declined. Dr. Salk still devotes long hours to perfecting his vaccine, making it even more effective, more long-lived in the immunity it confers.

Meanwhile Albert Sabin continued to work on his live-virus vaccine. The Salk vaccine had done wonders, everyone agreed—even Dr. Sabin. But it was not a really satisfactory long-term polio enemy. The live virus vaccine had many advantages. It could be taken by mouth, instead of being injected. It would give near-permanent immunity against polio. It would be simpler and cheaper to produce and to administer than the Salk vaccine.

In 1962 the Sabin vaccine was licensed for public use. But almost immediately one of the types of Sabin vaccine ran into problems and had to be withdrawn. After further testing, the Sabin vaccine was once again made available, and it and several other oral polio vaccines are now in widespread use.

Nonetheless it was Dr. Salk who brought the foe down. Polio is becoming a disease of the past wherever the vaccine has reached. The cases of polio today are isolated and few, and we can look forward to a time when this paralyzing killer passes completely out of our lives and into the annals of medical history.

15

Lillehei: Within the Open Heart

THE HEART is a pump. It is fashioned mostly out of muscle
—thick, tough muscle. There is nothing fragile about the heart. It is
designed to do its work for seventy to one hundred years without missing a beat. No man-made pump can match the record of the human
heart, ceaselessly and tirelessly pumping blood to every part of the
body for decade after decade.

But the heart is also the master organ of the body. It has the re-
sponsibility for sustaining life, for sending the all-important blood
through the organism. Let the heart cease its work for a few moments
and the brain succumbs to oxygen starvation, the other organs stop
functioning, all the processes of life are irreversibly halted—in short,
death is the result.

This being the case, how could heart surgery be possible? Anything that might interfere with the beating of the heart would cause
death.

The first hesitant approaches to heart surgery came by way of pus
drainage. The heart is surrounded by a double layer of membrane,
the pericardium. Certain diseases cause the pericardium to fill with
fluid, which can then become infected. As early as 1850, the surgeon
Bernhard von Langenbeck ventured to open a patient's chest to drain
pus from the pericardial cavity. Several other operations of this kind
were performed in the next four decades.

Meanwhile, in 1882, it had been shown that a wound in a rabbit's heart could be stitched and the rabbit would live. Other experimental work followed, in the hope that some day surgeons would be able to stitch a wound in a human heart.

Some surgeons flatly declared that it was impossible and almost blasphemous to try to stitch a human heart. The great German surgeon Billroth, a pioneer in abdominal surgery, bluntly stated, "The surgeon who would attempt to suture a wound in the heart would lose the respect of his colleagues."

Nevertheless the attempt was made. In 1895, a Norwegian, Axel Cappelen, stitched a heart wound caused by a dagger stab. An Italian, Guido Farina, attempted the same thing a year later. Both operations failed. But in September, 1896, the surgeon Louis Rehn of Frankfort stitched a wound in the right side of a man's heart, and the man lived.

It was all the more amazing, because 36 hours had passed between the time the wound was made and the time it was repaired. The "impossible" operation had been performed. The medical conservatives were taken aback.

"Very well," they conceded. "It's possible to stitch a heart. But not to perform surgery on it!"

In the vocabulary of science, "impossible" is a word without much meaning. But it took a while before surgeons could actually begin working within the heart.

One of the first steps came in 1901. A doctor found that he could massage the heart of a patient who had died on the operating table, and thus restore life. It often happens that a patient's heart stops beating during even a minor operation. This bold discovery turned many surgeons into miracle-workers.

About the same time, another physician worked out an operation for a disease of the pericardium wherein that membrane adheres to the chest wall and affects the action of the heart. This led to a series of operations on the pericardium, culminating in 1913 with an actual removal of the membrane.

In that same year a surgeon named Eugene Doyen brought the

knife inside the heart itself. This was in an operation for stenosis, or obstruction, of one of the valves of the heart. Doyen entered through the right side of the heart and divided the stenotic valve. Unfortunately, the patient died, but an autopsy showed she could not have survived the operation under any circumstances.

World War I gave surgeons a number of opportunities to experiment with heart surgery. They worked on men near death, who could not be saved at all. But little was accomplished. One problem was that the pericardium tended to fill with blood after the heart had been wounded. The surgeon, cutting through the pericardium to reach the heart, would be greeted by a wild spurt of blood that often would drench him completely, hiding the heart from view.

One surgeon, Rudolph Matas, described it this way:

> The operator must thrust his fingers into the pericardial sac through the swirl of blood and endeavor to locate the wound . . . or he must grasp the heart with his whole hand and drag the bleeding, writhing organ . . . out . . . where, by gradually relaxing his grasp, the seat of the hemorrhage will certainly be identified and the suture readily applied.

Suturing of heart wounds gradually became more frequent, despite such things, and the mortality rate dropped from 40 percent or more to a moderate figure. But little was done in the way of real heart surgery.

The heart operation that is generally considered to be the first triumph of modern heart surgery was performed in Boston, in 1938, by Dr. Robert E. Gross. This was a *ductus arteriosus* operation.

The ductus arteriosus is a small blood vessel which, in the unborn child, connects the aorta, or main artery, to the pulmonary artery that carries used blood to the lungs. Since the lungs of an unborn child are inactive, there is no reason to circulate blood through them. The ductus arteriosus diverts the child's blood away from the lungs and into the placenta, the membrane of the womb, where it is reoxygenated. After birth, the ductus normally shrivels up and withers away.

Sometimes, though, it fails to disappear. It remains open. But now the child's lungs are functioning and the placenta is gone. Blood should go from the pulmonary artery to the lungs every time the lungs expand. But if the ductus remains, it serves as an unwanted outlet for used blood that should be going straight to the lungs. It sidetracks the blood and sends it back to the aorta, where it must make the cycle all over again, still failing to pick up a fresh oxygen supply.

Often the effect of the abnormality is slight. It goes unnoticed. Most of the blood still makes the normal cycle from the aorta to the lungs, and only a small quantity dribbles off through the ductus arteriosus and back into the aorta. But sometimes as much as 70 percent of the blood is diverted. Thus the body is robbed of oxygen. Anyone with such a condition is condemned to early death.

Gross succeeded in tying off the duct. Later, he improved on his technique by actually removing a section of the duct, making a reopening impossible. Today, ductus arteriosus operations are performed on hundreds of children each year. Few die.

This pioneering operation heralded a new era in heart surgery. The next big leap came in 1944, when Gross and Clarence Crafoord of Stockholm, working independently, operated on blockages of the aorta. Later that year, Alfred Blalock and Helen Taussig of Johns Hopkins performed the first "blue baby" operation.

Blue babies are born with malformed hearts. They cannot get enough oxygen into their blood. Through surgery, Blalock and Taussig were able to direct blood from the aorta to the lungs—in effect the reverse of Gross' ductus operation.

From 1948 on, surgery inside the heart itself became a regular fact. The Gross, Blalock-Taussig, and Crafoord operations had all dealt with the blood vessels just outside the heart. Now, doctors such as Charles Bailey of Philadelphia and Dwight Harken of Harvard began to work *within* the heart.

They were operating in cases of mitral stenosis—narrowing of the mitral valve of the heart. They used tiny knives attached to their fingertips. The finger was inserted in the heart, and the valve leaflets were split apart with the knife. The surgeon could not see into the heart. He had to depend on his sense of touch.

Since 1948 this operation has been performed tens of thousands of times. But the surgeon always has to work blind, unable to see the site of the operation. Such a closed-heart operation was highly difficult to perform, and not always possible in every case.

"If only we could lay bare the heart," surgeons wished. "If we could operate under direct vision!"

A method called *hypothermia* provided a way. Hypothermia is the lowering of the body temperature. In 1950, a Toronto doctor showed that when a patient's body temperature is sharply reduced, the brain cells and other body cells have less demand for oxygen than otherwise. Thus the circulation of the blood can be temporarily stopped without fear of immediate death. The brain could be deprived of blood for as much as 15 minutes, other parts of the body for up to an hour. The body remained in a kind of suspended animation while the surgeon worked.

The age of open-heart surgery began in 1952. Dr. John Lewis of the University of Minnesota performed the trail-blazing operation. A five-year-old girl had a leak between the auricles of her heart. Her body temperature was brought down to 82 degrees by plunging her into a bath of cold water. Her chest was opened. The veins that carry blood to the heart were clamped. Since the heart went on beating, it emptied itself of blood in a few moments.

The surgeon, working on a dry and exposed heart, quickly performed the operation, repairing the leak. After five and a half minutes he was finished. The circulation of the blood was turned back on. The patient was immersed in a tub of warm water and her temperature was brought back to normal.

It was a phenomenal surgical feat. But hypothermia was seen to have several serious drawbacks. For one, it involved subjecting the patient to violent shifts in body temperatures. Someone already weakened by illness could not take such treatment. For another, the surgeon had, at best, only five to eight minutes in which to operate. Beyond that point there was great risk of brain damage.

This meant that complex heart surgery could not be performed at all under hypothermia. Only the simplest of adjustments could be made. Also, any unexpected complication could be fatal, since the surgeon would not have time to cope with it properly.

So hypothermia had only limited value, astonishing development though it was. Medical researchers concentrated on something else which seemed even more fantastic—building an artificial heart, which would continue to circulate blood through the patient while the real heart underwent an operation that might last an hour or more!

Such work dated back as far as the 1930's. It was seen at the outset that the machine would have to play the part of lungs as well as heart, oxygenating the blood as well as pumping it through the blood vessels. This proved difficult. Pumps are easy things to build; lungs are not. The lungs are tremendously complex, with a vast surface area. A normal 150-pound adult has some 600 square feet of lung surface for passing oxygen into the blood stream and taking carbon dioxide out.

So any artificial lung would have to be big. Dr. John H. Gibbon of the Jefferson Medical College, who had begun research into heart-lung machines in 1937, solved the problem by using stainless-steel screens in an atmosphere of pure oxygen. The blood is passed in a thin film over these screens. Other researchers built machines on similar principles, using rotating disks instead of screens.

Once the problem of how to oxygenate the blood was solved, the rest was relatively simple. Pumps were built. Dogs were used for the first tests. The heart-lung machine was connected to the dog's heart at three places—to the two main veins that supply blood to the heart, and to the aorta that carries blood from the heart to the body. The heart was bypassed completely. Blood circulated through the artificial heart and thence to the body.

In 1953 Dr. Gibbon performed the first artificial heart operation on a human being. An 18-year-old girl was connected to the machine and a large defect in her heart was successfully repaired.

But several other operations immediately afterward failed. Many surgeons came to feel that the heart-lung machine would not be suitable for human beings, however well it might work on dogs. They blamed this not on the machine, which clearly was capable of sustaining life, but on the patients. Humans, it seemed, simply could not tolerate the triple shock of having their hearts opened, having their blood circulated outside their body, and having surgery performed on the heart structure.

At the University of Minnesota, however, the research staff remained optimistic. The man in charge here was Dr. C. Walton Lillehei. Born in Minneapolis in 1918, Dr. Lillehei had served as an army doctor in World War II, winning a Bronze Star for his work under fire on the Anzio beachhead. Then he had returned to Minneapolis to study surgery. In 1951, he began to specialize in heart surgery.

He and his staff discovered, again by experimenting on dogs, that it was not necessary to maintain a normal rate of circulation through a heart-lung machine. A circulation of 10 to 15 percent of normal was enough to sustain life. This "low-flow" principle, making less of a demand on the patient, opened new possibilities for artificial circulation methods.

A casual remark by a member of Lillehei's staff led to the next development. Herbert E. Warden was the man who said one day that he wished "patients could be plugged into an oxygen supply the way an unborn child is plugged into its mother."

"Why not?" someone else asked.

Lillehei soon found himself seriously considering an amazing substitute for the heart-lung machine: an actual human being!

This new technique was known as "cross-circulation"—the pumping of the patient's blood through the body of a donor, who would oxygenate it through his own heart and lungs, and return it to the patient's body. The first experiments, with dogs, were successful. Blood could be circulated between pairs of dogs, the blood flowing at up to 30 percent of the normal speed, without harm to either animal.

The first surgery with human cross-circulation took place in Dr.

Lillehei's operating room in March, 1954. The patient was a year-old baby with a serious heart defect. The donor was the child's father.

Father and child lay side by side on two operating tables. Oxygenated blood from an artery in the father's thigh passed to a pump, and then to a tube which entered an artery in the chest of the baby. The blood then passed through the child's body, bypassing the heart, and left through another set of tubes and pumps, returning to a vein in the father's thigh.

The operation lasted 17½ minutes. Throughout, the father's heart and lungs did the work for both. The heart defect was successfully corrected. However, 11 days after the operation, the baby died of pneumonia.

Two other children were successfully operated on by the same method that same week. Forty-two more cross-circulation operations were carried out by Dr. Lillehei and his associates in the months that followed. Many of the operations were highly successful. Even so, the operations were risky for the donor. The Minnesota group looked for yet another method of performing open-heart operations.

The next step was the use of an animal's lung as the oxygenator. A lung was carefully removed from an anesthetized laboratory dog, and was completely cleansed of animal blood. Then it was placed in a plastic container and linked by plastic tubes to a mechanical pump.

A 13-year-old boy who had suffered severe heart injuries was the first patient. His blood was drawn from his body and passed into the oxygen-filled plastic container. The dog lung served to oxygenate the blood before it returned to the boy's body. For twenty minutes his heart was bypassed. The operation was successful. Fourteen others like it followed.

In 1955, however, Lillehei's group, always searching for better ways of performing the open-heart operation, perfected a new, completely mechanical circulator. This was known as the *helix-reservoir* system. It is safer and more flexible than any of the previous methods. It needs no disks or screens. Oxygen is bubbled into the blood, and the surface of the bubbles themselves provides the needed surface area for exchanging oxygen and carbon dioxide.

The helix-reservoir system, and others like it, are now in general use. Today, surgeons work on the exposed heart with an ease and a taken-for-granted casualness that would have seemed breathtaking as recently as 1954. The patient's heart can be started and stopped at will, and the most intricate of operations can be performed.

Open-heart operations today are routine matters. Fifty to seventy of them are performed *every day* in the United States alone. Just a few years ago, each open-heart operation was cause for headlines, but not any longer.

Open-heart operations are sometimes performed under local anesthesia, the patient remaining conscious and aware. More usually, though, a complete anesthetic is used, as well as curare or some other drug that relaxes the heart muscle. A team of a dozen or more surgeons, nurses, and assistants takes part in each operation. The oxygenator that serves as the patient's heart and lungs must be primed with half a dozen pints of blood or so, and this is usually contributed by medical students at the hospital where the operation is to take place.

The first stage in the operation, after anesthesia has taken effect, is to make the chest incision and lay open the chest cavity. Plastic tubes are readied for insertion in the arteries and veins. The ribs are spread, the pericardium is cut, and the oxygenator is connected to the blood vessels.

The patient's heart is then "turned off" and empties itself. For half an hour or more, the surgeons can work on the dry heart. One danger at this point is *fibrillation,* in which the beating heart "runs away"—its regular beat turning into a wild, chaotic spasming that gives it the appearance, as one surgeon describes it, of "a bag of worms."

Fibrillation is fatal if not halted at once. But in any open-heart operation an electric defibrillator stands by, ready to deliver an electric shock that will stop the runaway spasming. The heart can then be restarted with ease and its regular beat restored.

On—off. Just like a light switch!

I am tempted to wonder, after seeing a color film of an open-heart operation, just what old Vesalius or Ambroise Paré would have had to say, if they were plucked from the Middle Ages and permitted to look on.

They were both hard-headed, unsuperstitious men. But I think they both would have suspected that black magic was at work!

Postscript

We are at the end of our book, but not at the end of the story of medicine. That story has no end. So long as there is disease, so long as there is death, there will be medical research, and there will be new great doctors coming forth to take their place with Hippocrates and Galen and John Hunter and the rest of that splendid crew.

The dazzling accomplishments of the last century mark not a climax but a beginning of the great age of medicine. Cancer, arteriosclerosis, cerebral palsy, even the common cold—all these await their final conquest. Those conquests will come. There is no reason to think that any medical problem will remain insoluble forever.

So the ranks of the great doctors have some room left. The new Harvey Cushing, the new Edward Jenner, the new Jonas Salk—these men will be coming along. I like to think that some of them, their great accomplishments still in the future, are reading this very page.

Bibliography

THERE ARE more volumes on the history of medicine than there are words in this book—by far. I could not begin to list even the most famous here, unless I wanted to add many hundreds of pages to this book.

What I have done, instead, is to compile a list of those books that have been most useful to me in writing *The Great Doctors,* and also those books which will offer the greatest benefit to the reader who wants to go on from my brief introduction to the history of medicine, who wants to read the full, detailed stories of the doctors whose lives I have had to compress into a few pages each.

First, some general books on the history of medicine:

Castiglioni, Arturo, *A History of Medicine* (1947).

Garrison, F. H., *An Introduction to the History of Medicine* (1929).

Graham, Harvey, *Surgeons All* (1939).

Major, Ralph H., *A History of Medicine* (1954).

Sigerist, Henry, *A History of Medicine,* Volume 1 (1951); Volume 2 (1961).

Young, Agatha, *Scalpel* (1956).

In addition, *A History of Science,* by George Sarton (Volume 1, 1952; Volume 2, 1959) contains much valuable information on early medicine through the time of the Greeks and Romans.

There are two important books of source material which were recently restored to print by Dover Books, Inc. as paperbacks, and which contain many of the basic writings of the great doctors in good translations and with excellent editorial introductions. Many of the quotations in this book have been drawn from these two. They are:

Classics of Medicine and Surgery, edited by C. N. B. Camac.
Source Book of Medical History, edited by Logan Clendening.

For the individual doctors of this book, the following titles can be consulted:

HIPPOCRATES

The works of Hippocrates are available in an English translation by W. H. S. Jones, in the Loeb Classical Library (1923).

Selected works are to be found in Clendening, cited above.

Volume 2 of Sigerist, cited above, and Volume 1 of Sarton, cited above, have detailed and lengthy studies of Greek medicine with special emphasis on Hippocrates.

GALEN

A good biography of Galen, with an essay on his work, is *Galen of Pergamon,* by George Sarton (1954).

Selections from his writings are to be found in Clendening. There is an extensive translation by A. J. Brock in the Loeb Classical Library (1923).

VESALIUS

The best biographies of Vesalius in English are out of print and hard to find. They are:

The Life and Work of Andreas Vesalius, by Hermann and Albinus Boerhaave (1930).
A Bio-Bibliography of Andreas Vesalius, by Harvey Cushing (1943).
In Defence of Vesalius, by F. H. Garrison (1916).
Andreas Vesalius and His Time, by George Piersol (1915–16).

The preface to the *Fabrica* is in Clendening. There is no complete translation of the *Fabrica* in English, but there are several recent volumes of selections of the illustrations, and a very expensive facsimile of the original Latin text was issued before World War II.

PARÉ

There are many good biographies of Paré. They include:
Life and Times of Ambroise Paré, by F. R. Packard (1921).

Ambroise Paré and His Times, by Stephen Paget (1897).

Selections from the Works of Ambroise Paré, with Short Biography, by
    D. W. Singer (1924).

There are excerpts from Paré's works in Clendening. The best collection
of Paré's writings is *Apology and Treatise of Ambroise Paré Containing
the Voyages Made into Divers Places with Many of His Writings upon
Surgery,* edited and with introduction by Geoffrey Langdon Keynes (1951).

HARVEY

William Harvey, by D'Arcy Power (1897).

The Personality of William Harvey, by Geoffrey Langdon Keynes
    (1949).

Brief Lives, by John Aubrey (reprinted 1957).

The Discovery of the Circulation of the Blood, by Charles Singer (1922).

The complete text of *De Motu Cordis,* translated into English, can be
found in Camac, cited above.

HUNTER

An excellent recent biography of John Hunter is *The Reluctant Surgeon,*
by John Kobler (1960). There are also these earlier works:

Hunter, the Founder of Scientific Surgery, by Edgar L. Gilchrest (1933).

John Hunter, Man of Science and Surgeon, by Stephen Paget (1898).

John Hunter, a Martyr to Science, by D'Arcy Power (1925).

An excerpt from Hunter's *On Venereal Diseases* is included in Clendening. Hunter's own writings are long out of print and hard to obtain.

JENNER

The Life of Edward Jenner, by F. D. Drewitt (1931).

Jenner and Vaccination, by Charles Creighton (1889).

Smallpox and Vaccination, by B. White (1924).

The complete text of Jenner's book on vaccination is to be found in
Camac.

McDOWELL

*Ephraim McDowell, Father of the Ovariotomy and Founder of Abdom-
    inal Surgery,* by August Schachner (1921).

The Biography of Ephraim McDowell, by Mary T. Valentine (1890).

MORTON

The story of the discovery of anesthesia, with all its twists and turns, is best told in *Victory over Pain,* by Victor Robinson, M.D. (1946). These are some of the other books that cover the same ground:

The History of Surgical Anesthesia, by Thomas E. Keys (1945).

Crawford W. Long, by Frances Long Taylor (Long's daughter). (1928).

Man Against Pain, by Howard Riley Raper (1945).

Camac's *Classics of Medicine and Surgery* contains Morton's original pamphlet, *Remarks on the Proper Mode of Administering Sulphuric Ether by Inhalation,* along with a later article of Morton's and many letters and comments on the controversy. The same excellent anthology includes James Young Simpson's account of chloroform as a substitute for ether in anesthesia, first published in 1848.

LISTER

The Centenary of Lister, a Tale of Sepsis and Antisepsis, by P. C. A. Ashurst (1927).

Lord Lister, by J. R. Godlee (1917).

A Mirror for Surgeons, by D'Arcy Power (1939).

Joseph, Baron Lister, by A. L. Turner (1927).

The best edition of Lister's own works, rather hard to find, is *Six Papers by Lord Lister, with a Biography and Explanatory Notes,* edited by J. R. Godlee (1921).

There are excerpts from several of Lister's papers in Clendening. Camac includes the complete text of "On the Antiseptic Principle in the Practice of Surgery."

REED

The standard biography of Walter Reed is quite old—*Walter Reed and Yellow Fever,* by H. A. Kelly (1906). Paul de Kruif's colorful and famous *Microbe Hunters* (1926) has a good chapter on Reed.

An excerpt from Reed's own account of the yellow fever fight is included in Clendening.

HALSTED

William Stewart Halsted, by W. G. MacCallum (1930) is the definitive biography.

CUSHING

There are two biographies of Cushing, one long, one short, both outstanding. They are:

Harvey Cushing, a Biography, by John F. Fulton (1946).

Harvey Cushing, Surgeon, Author, Artist, by Elizabeth H. Thompson (1950).

Cushing's own writings on medicine and on books are hard to come by. But many libraries and bookstores have copies of his great *Life of Sir William Osler* (1926). Although Cushing was one of Osler's closest friends for many years, he carefully does not mention his own name once in the book—but it is a marvelous, though extremely lengthy, work that tells us much not only about Osler but about Halsted, Welch, Kelly, Johns Hopkins at the turn of the century, and the world of medicine from 1870 to 1920.

SALK

Jonas Salk's medical career is far from over, and his definitive biography is yet to be written. Two important documents on the Salk vaccine are to be found in a paperback published by Dell Books in 1956, *New Worlds of Modern Science,* edited by Leonard Engel. These are Dr. Salk's own article, "Studies in Human Subjects on Active Immunization against Poliomyelitis," and a synopsis of Dr. Francis' report on the 1954 mass field trial of Salk vaccine. Also see Dr. Salk's article in *Scientific American,* April 1955: "Vaccines for Poliomyelitis."

LILLEHEI

There is not much available yet on open-heart surgery or the work of C. Walton Lillehei. But see *The Operation,* by Leonard Engel (1958) for a good report on the state of such surgery through that year.

Two magazine articles are also useful. These are: "Hypothermia" by Raymond J. Hock and Benjamin G. Covino, in *Scientific American,* March 1958; and "Open-Heart Surgery," by C. Walton Lillehei and Leonard Engel, *Scientific American,* February, 1960.

Index

The Author

ROBERT SILVERBERG has been a full-time free-lance writer since he graduated from Columbia University in 1956. However, he began writing professionally in 1953 and had his first book published when he was in his junior year at college. Mr. Silverberg originally specialized in science fiction, but nowadays he concentrates on books of non-fiction dealing with historical, archaeological, and scientific subjects. In 1963 Putnam published his *15 Battles That Changed the World*. Several of Mr. Silverberg's books have been selections of the Junior Literary Guild, the Teen Age Book Club, and the Literary Guild, Young Adult Division. He, his wife and their four cats live in a huge, book-filled old house once owned by Fiorello LaGuardia, in Riverdale, New York.